Ms. Sanders
44A East Dulwich Roa
London
SE12 9AX

CW00429454

PROFESSIONAL COUNSELOR HANDBOOKS

Volume

I

SOBRIETY DEMYSTIFIED

GETTING CLEAN AND SOBER WITH NLP AND CBT

Byron A. Lewis, M.A.

1996
Kelsey & Co.
Publishing

SOBRIETY DEMYSTIFIED:
GETTING CLEAN AND SOBER WITH NLP AND CBT
Byron A. Lewis, M.A.

Copyright © 1994 by Byron A. Lewis

All rights reserved. No part of this book may be utilized in any form or by any means, electronic or mechanical, including photocopying, recording, or by any other information storage or retreival system, without permission in writing from the author.

Published by:

Kelsey & Co.
Publishing
P.O. Box 1138
Santa Cruz, CA 95061-1138

Illustrations by Leslie Lewis
Layout & design and cover design by Peter Greenbaum-Knight
Printed in the United States of America

Library of Congress Cataloging-in-Publication Data
Lewis, Byron A.
Sobriety Demystified: Getting Clean and Sober with NLP and CBT / Byron A. Lewis
Includes bibliographic references and index.
ISBN 1-887338-00-4
Library of Congress Catalog Card Number: 96-75578

FIRST PRINTING, 1996

ACKNOWLEDGMENTS

Thanks go to many people without whom this volume would never have been written. Richard Bandler and John Grinder initiated me into the exciting field of NLP, and my early teachers including Leslie Cameron-Bandler and Frank Pucelik helped open my senses to life's many experiences. The U.S. Army's Alcohol and Drug Abuse Prevention and Control Program (ADAPCP) offered me the forum to learn and grow in the field of addictions counseling. James Ronan, Jr. persistently encouraged my expansion from the limits of the system and exploration into the realms of possibility. Jancy Limpert and Carla Jones provided major editing, and their input helped immeasurably in creating the final draft. It was Bob Gardner's printer that enabled me to view and edit the original manuscript. Finally, thanks to Leslie Lewis for her editing, suggestions and the creative illustrations which grace these pages.

CONTENTS

Acknowledgements ⋯⋯⋯⋯⋯⋯⋯⋯⋯⋯⋯⋯⋯⋯ v
Preface ⋯⋯⋯⋯⋯⋯⋯⋯⋯⋯⋯⋯⋯⋯⋯⋯⋯⋯ xi
Introduction ⋯⋯⋯⋯⋯⋯⋯⋯⋯⋯⋯⋯⋯⋯⋯ xiii

1 Neuro-linguistic Programming as a Cognitive-behavioral Therapy ⋯⋯⋯⋯⋯⋯⋯⋯ 1
    CBT Defined ⋯⋯⋯⋯⋯⋯⋯⋯⋯⋯⋯⋯⋯⋯ 2
    NLP Defined ⋯⋯⋯⋯⋯⋯⋯⋯⋯⋯⋯⋯⋯⋯ 3
    Schematic of the Two Models ⋯⋯⋯⋯⋯⋯⋯ 4
    The Origins of CBT ⋯⋯⋯⋯⋯⋯⋯⋯⋯⋯⋯ 5
    The Origins of NLP ⋯⋯⋯⋯⋯⋯⋯⋯⋯⋯⋯ 7
    NLP as a CBT ⋯⋯⋯⋯⋯⋯⋯⋯⋯⋯⋯⋯⋯ 8
    Internal Dialogue ⋯⋯⋯⋯⋯⋯⋯⋯⋯⋯⋯ 11
    Notes for Chapter 1 ⋯⋯⋯⋯⋯⋯⋯⋯ 13

2 The Emergent Paradigm ⋯⋯⋯⋯⋯⋯⋯⋯⋯ 15
    Confusion in the Field ⋯⋯⋯⋯⋯⋯⋯⋯⋯ 16
    Models of Addiction ⋯⋯⋯⋯⋯⋯⋯⋯⋯⋯ 17
    Morality Versus the Drug Issue ⋯⋯⋯⋯⋯ 19
    The American Disease Model ⋯⋯⋯⋯⋯⋯ 21
    Alchoholics Anonymous ⋯⋯⋯⋯⋯⋯⋯⋯ 22
    Psychoanalytic Models ⋯⋯⋯⋯⋯⋯⋯⋯⋯ 24
    The Behavioral Model ⋯⋯⋯⋯⋯⋯⋯⋯⋯ 26
    Biological Models ⋯⋯⋯⋯⋯⋯⋯⋯⋯⋯⋯ 27
    Social Learning Theory Model ⋯⋯⋯⋯⋯⋯ 28
    Cognitive Behavioral Models ⋯⋯⋯⋯⋯⋯ 30
    The Damaged Brain Model ⋯⋯⋯⋯⋯⋯⋯ 31
    Multidimensional Cravings Model ⋯⋯⋯⋯ 33
    A Unified Approach ⋯⋯⋯⋯⋯⋯⋯⋯⋯⋯ 34
    Final Words ⋯⋯⋯⋯⋯⋯⋯⋯⋯⋯⋯⋯⋯ 35
    Notes for Chapter 2 ⋯⋯⋯⋯⋯⋯⋯⋯ 36

3 Assessment and Motivation ⋯⋯⋯⋯⋯⋯ 37
    Defining Addiction ⋯⋯⋯⋯⋯⋯⋯⋯⋯⋯ 38
    Use, Abuse, or Dependence ⋯⋯⋯⋯⋯⋯ 40

Definitions from the Field 41
The Loss of Control Issue 44
The Role of Denial 46
Abstinence vs. Moderation 49
Polydrug Abuse and Other Compulsions 53
Motivation 54
What Motivation is Not 55
What is Motivation? 58
Stage Model of Motivation 59
Motivation and Treatment Planning 65
Notes for Chapter 3 67

4 Twelve Step Programs **71**
The Meeting 73
A Brief History 75
Why It Works 76
Prescription for Physical Addiction 76
Prescription for Psychological Distress 77
Prescription for Social Reintegration 77
Prescription for Spiritual Growth 78
Logical Levels of Change Model 81
How It Works 81
The Twelve Steps 82
Taking the First Three Steps 107
Ninety Meetings in Ninety Days 108
AA is Not for Everybody 108
Rational Recovery 109
Secular Organizations for Sobriety 112
Notes for Chapter 4 113

5 Irrational Thought **117**
Beginning the Work 118
Rapport 118
Therapeutic Outcomes 121
Cognitive Distortions 123
The NLP Meta Model 124
Cognitive Errors 131
RET Disputational Techniques 136
Five Rational Questions of RBT 138

The Cookie-Cutter Mind 139
Notes for Chapter 5 145

6 Irrational Beliefs **147**
Beliefs About Beliefs 147
Impacting Beliefs 149
Irrational Strategies 151
The Syntax of RET and RBT 154
The Using-To-Cope Strategy 155
The Worthless Relapser Strategy 158
The Excitement Imperative Strategy 160
Nine Disputation Strategies of RET 162
The Goal of RET 164
NLP Approaches 166
Belief Molecules 167
Notes for Chapter 6 176

7 Identity and Beyond **179**
Working in the Present 180
Working in the Past 184
NLP and Dysfunctional Belief Systems 187
Defining the Imprint 187
Reframing the Intentions 191
Building a New Experience 193
Working with the Future 197
Creating a Future Self-image 198
Completing an Inventory 199
Painting the Future 201
The Adventure of Recovery 202
Notes for Chapter 7 204

Appendix 1: The Abbreviated Meta Model **207**
Appendix 2: NLP Accessing Cues **211**
Appendix 3: Sub-Modalities **217**
Appendix 4: Resources **219**
References **221**
Index **229**
Upcoming Works **235**
Ordering and Information **238**

As I approached the conclusion of the first draft of this book, I realized a special introduction was warranted. I've been working with neuro-linguistic programming (NLP) practically since its inception. During the last eight years, I have also applied various techniques from the field of cognitive-behavioral therapy (CBT) to my work in addictions counseling. For some time, now, I have felt the desire to write a book marrying these fields.

I'm not a pretentious person. I was even denied a job once based on the fact that I asked for *too low* a starting salary! However, during the last ten years or so, I have watched an unnecessary schism develop and grow between NLP and CBT. Having worked with both approaches, I am acutely aware of the great similarities between the two schools. It has bothered me for some time that no one has had the inclination to bring this to light. Inspired by the dearth of material linking NLP with CBT, I wrote certain sections to address this issue head on. Of course, the major theme of this book is understanding and working with addiction and other compulsive disorders. Those interested in these areas will find this book a practical addition to their store of information.

The primary audience I have in mind is the practicing counselor, therapist, or NLP practitioner working with drug addicts, alcoholics, and other mood-altering, compulsive disorders. For the sake of clarity, the following are brief definitions for readers who may be unfamiliar with the above terms, disciplines, or practices.

1. **Addiction**: In general terms, addiction refers to a compulsively repeated pattern of behavior (usually involving the use of mood-altering chemicals) which causes alterations in the chemistry of the brain of the addict and/or in his mood or emotional state.

2. **Counselor**: From the writings of Philip Beebe (1990), comes the most applicable definition I have yet found. A counselor is "Any individual who works in a therapeutic or counseling situation regardless of the title of the position. This includes licensed and unlicensed individuals as well as clergy, lay and paraprofessional workers." (p. 34)

3. **Neuro-linguistic programming (NLP)**: In its most basic form, NLP defines functional connections between the brain (neuro) and language (linguistic), then uses this foundation to provide tools for effecting changes in our behavior (programming).

4. **NLP Practitioner**: This refers to an individual who has completed specific training conducted by licensed NLP Trainers and is certified to provide counseling using NLP techniques.

5. **Cognitive-behavioral therapy (CBT)**: There are several different definitions of this relatively new addition to the field of psychology. In its essence, CBT is a blend of strategies that focus on a client's thought processes to affect therapeutic change.

We should be bold in what we try

and cautious in what we claim

(Neal Miller, 1974, p.9).

IN THE BEGINNING

The drive up Alba Road wound through the redwoods and pines. On this, the "shady side" of the Santa Cruz mountains, it was always cooler if not downright cold. The call had come again as it always did. "Hi, Byron. It's John. Want to come up and work with someone?" No big, long-winded analytic discussion of the client's "presenting problem." No review of his course of treatment. Just a chance to "play" with the budding techniques of neuro-linguistic programming (NLP), to "experiment" with one of Richard Bandler or John Grinder's current innovative brainstorms from their modeling of master

THE DRIVE UP ALBA

therapists and communicators. "I'll be right up," was always my response to these calls. It was great being a student in those days. Aside from classes at UCSC and working nights as a waiter, I had few other commitments.

On my arrival, John briefly reviewed with me the client's problem, suggested a few techniques, and pointed me toward the door to the "therapy room" with instructions to report back on the results of the intervention. Usually working on some project or another, he returned to his writing or reading. I worked with clients under the mandate, "If what you're doing isn't working, try something else!" I was taught to have faith in my clients' ability to generate the internal resources needed to make the therapeutic changes they were seeking. It became my responsibility to create the environment for the client to tap these resources.

I was fortunate to have been introduced to therapy as an adventure and as an opportunity to explore the limits of personal boundaries. I was taught to break the boundaries which limit a person's growth or cause pain using NLP's extremely effective overt and covert manipulations of thought, perceptions, and beliefs. I never feared the encounters, because my practicum was not constricted by worries of "doing it right" or of "messing them up more" as are so many students of social work and psychology I have known. I was absolutely free to expand both my client's boundaries and my own at the same time: "Therapy is for the therapist" was one of the precepts of the process. I have never forgotten that sense of freedom, that magical joy of changing and growing along with those clients at the top of Alba Drive.

THE ESTRANGEMENT OF NLP

Many shifts which occurred after those early creative days[1] appear to have strayed somewhat from the original principles guiding my practice of NLP therapy. There was increased emphasis on "techniques" in NLP training and books. This was followed by a period of turbulent "disenfranchising" of the various groups of NLPers. Those events, combined with the "bad press" surrounding some of the more flamboyant NLP practitioners, caused many from mainstream established schools of psychology to look with disdain upon this new brand of "pop psychology."

Complicating matters was the separation NLPers fostered in their own writings that stressed how their new discipline differed from the others. In fact, it almost appears that the estrangement of NLP from mainstream psychology was initiated by the originators of NLP themselves. In their preface to *NLP Volume I* (whose contributors read as a *Who's Who* of early NLP: Robert Dilts, John Grinder, Richard Bandler, Leslie Cameron-Bandler and Judith DeLozier, 1980), the authors wrote, "We wish at this point to separate our NLP from the many fields from which it draws information, from the many fields for which it has application." They also go on to point out the differences in their new technology: "NLP differs from other models of behavior in that it is specifically a model of our behavior as model-makers. It is what we call a meta-model, a model of the modeling process itself" (p. 5). This book also set a precedent which may have contributed to mainstream psychologist's reluctance to accept NLP: they made rather extravagant claims like, "As the tools of NLP find their ways into other fields and the number of NLPers increases, we will witness in our life-time marvels as grandiose as a man on the moon, the permanent elimination of smallpox from the planet earth, and atomic power" (Dilts, et. al., 1980, p. ii).

Some of the later writers in the field continued to set themselves apart by claiming extremely high expectations for their "new" technology. One very popular NLP splinter group is composed of Leslie Cameron-Bandler, David Gordon, & Michael Lebeau. In their book *Know How* (1985b), these authors claimed "...Mental Aptitude Patterning and the products it has engendered hold the possibility for stimulating a renaissance of individual initiative, accomplishment, and evolution. The world may never be the same" (p. xi).[2] Wow!

As NLP's popularity grew during the 1980's, there was a tremendous gap to be hurdled by more traditional or mainstream psychotherapists, if they were to embrace it. The on-going elitist stance among NLP practitioners did little to promote its acceptance by traditional psychotherapists. Marilyn Darling (1988), who studied NLP during its formative years, noted that many NLPers tended to overstate their case when describing the applications of NLP. She writes, "They have made bold and unsubstantiated claims--phobia cures in 10 minutes, lifelong perfect pitch, etc. And they repeat mythic tales of power and wonder" (p. 38).[3] In her article written in *defense* of NLP, Darling points out that NLP simply hasn't lived up to many of its claims. However, neither have a number of other approaches to therapy. That doesn't stop therapists from using them, because these approaches *do* work at times with some of our clients or with particular problems!

Of course, NLPers are not alone in their enthusiastic chest-pounding. Albert Ellis, one of the giants in the field of cognitive-behavioral therapy (CBT), begins the introduction to his 1988 book about treating substance abusers with, "Originated by Albert Ellis in 1955, Rational-Emotive Therapy has become one of the most comprehensive, integrative, and popular schools of psychotherapy ever practiced..." (p. 1).[4] I thought that particular accolade belonged to the school of Freudian Psychoanalysis! In addition, Maxie Maultsby (1984), developer of Rational Behavior Therapy (RBT), writes, "No one RBT concept, insight, or technique alone can reproduce the excellent clinical results described in [my] book. Understandably, therefore, for consistent results like these, you must use all of RBT, the way it is described here" (p. 7). Somehow, I find myself wondering if that is indeed true (or, with apologies to Dr. Maultsby, if it is *factual*).

The aggrandizement of a new technology or new approach to old problems is not unusual. Traditionally, great breakthroughs in psychology (or in any field, for that matter) are heralded by their originators as the "final and ultimate approach." There is a reason for this exaltation, or it wouldn't happen so consistently. This process is important in the early development of a nascent technology. Setting the technology apart protects it from contamination by other theorems and models, and allows it the time and space to prove itself and discover just how effective it can be. It appears that early NLP writers knew this. In fact, the rationale for their self-imposed separation is most clearly defined in *NLP Vol. I*. The authors cite the need to "...have greater clarity and freedom to delineate NLP's own methodologies and basic purpose" (1980, Preface).

Historically, however, the field of cognitive-behavioral psychology has better *paced* the existing psychotherapeutic community than has NLP. Of course, this may be attributable to the fact that many of the primary figures in the development of CBT were themselves already well-established in the psychotherapeutic community. With the backing by such notables as Aaron Beck, Albert Ellis, Alan Marlatt, and many others, and through intensive well-documented research, CBT has established itself as an efficacious addition to psychology. NLP, on the other hand, has not been quite as fortunate. My concern is that NLP continues to be largely ignored by clinicians and researchers in psychology. In addition, I believe the separation of NLP from the larger mainstream school of CBT has been caused by people simply misunderstanding what these folks from Santa Cruz were up to.

WHERE TO FROM HERE?

I have long admired Meichenbaum's unpretentious way of presenting his research in CBT. Ironically, I purchased his book during the period of my most intensive study of NLP. At the time, however, I did not make the connections I am proposing in this volume. There were several goals I had in mind at the initiation of this project. As with my previous book, I wanted to dispel some of the "magic" and "myth" surrounding NLP. This book accomplishes

...I have no packages to sell, no instant cures, no panaceas. Instead, I offer a progress report by hopefully a sensitive, somewhat eclectic research-clinician. (Donald Meichenbaum, 1977, p. 15).

this by focusing on similarities and the relationship between NLP and the well-established and respected field of CBT.

It has been frustrating sitting on the sidelines (my last book, written with Frank Pucelik, was published in 1982!) watching the schism grow between NLP and mainstream psychology. I know very well the value of NLP in my own approach to therapy. Having worked extensively with rational-emotive therapy (RET) and rational-behavior therapy (RBT) *in combination with* NLP, I know these disciplines compliment one another. I can no longer allow such an effective set of tools—approaches to therapy which can augment any therapist's work—to be discounted by those who stand to benefit most.

Another important goal was to present information which could help demystify some of the processes involved in getting clean and sober. This goal arose from the major theme of my work over the last six years. I wanted to provide both the NLP Practitioner and the CBT therapist with a helpful reference for dealing with America's fastest growing health problem: addiction.

The tools I chose to include in this text, although far from comprehensive, are applicable to a broad spectrum of addictive behaviors, including alcoholism, and addiction to drugs, relationships, sex, gambling, entertainment, etc. Although the primary focus of the text is addiction to chemicals, I have attempted to show commonalties with other compulsive mood-altering activities.[5] Throughout the text, I generally use the terms *addiction* and *mood-altering activities*, unless specifically referring to drug addiction or alcoholism.

Over the years, as I continued reading the literature in this exciting field of counseling, I discovered a concept which is gaining wide acceptance among those working in addiction research and treatment. I used the foundation of this *emergent paradigm* to facilitate an *inclusive*, rather than an *exclusive*, mind-set towards the many differing theories of addiction and recovery.

Finally, I've learned a great deal over the years from my addicted clients. Underlying all else is the principle that recovery cannot progress until these clients accept that they have a problem. The next step is also critical. It is a form of *emotional surrender* which becomes the foundation upon which motivation and lifestyle changes required for recovery can be built. This means the clients must accept "defeat," accept that they have lost the battle to effectively control their addiction. John Lovern (1991) suggests that "Inducing a chemically dependent person to surrender involves 'shaking up' the relationship between conscious and unconscious processes" (p. 25). The various techniques presented in this book do just that.

Until clients are willing to surrender to their addiction, they will tenaciously hang on to the denial that accompanies addictive disorders. I have found, however, that intervening with the addictive process can occur at almost any point in its development. The key is to accurately assess the *stage* of the addiction, then provide the appropriate intervention *strategy* for that stage. In this book, I demonstrate how to utilize the client's personal belief system and motivational strategies to facilitate this process.

Obviously, this book cannot cover in full detail every NLP and CBT technique presented. Rather, it seeks to provide an overview of how and where these interventions can be applied in counseling the addicted client. References to the original sources for specific techniques being discussed are included. I recommend readers not familiar with them look them up and read about them in greater detail from their originators!

WHY NOW?

We continue to evolve. As therapists, our experience demonstrates what works and what doesn't. The time has come to integrate mainstream psychology and the immensely valuable tools and techniques of NLP. I believe this melding of NLP with CBT will provide a synergetic outcome: CBT adds to NLP the efficacy of research-proven technology while NLP expands upon and clarifies many CBT techniques.

I have seen people getting into this attitude with N.L.P. where they only want to do magic. The attitude is that 'If it takes you more than twenty minutes, you must have done it wrong.' But I can tell you that when I was working with my mother to assist her in her recovery from cancer, I wasn't using quick, slick tricks, and I don't want to use tricks when I work with anybody else (Robert Dilts, 1990, p. 58).

In closing, let me address one final question: Why write a book on counseling the addicted client? First, it has become rather chic to admit to being a recovering alcoholic or drug addict. In fact, this fad is causing some ripples in Alcoholics Anonymous circles because many celebrities are "coming out of the closet" with their sobriety and admitting they are recovering from alcoholism or addiction through AA.[6] This violates the AA tradition of anonymity and focuses attention on the "personality" rather than the "disease".

Second, many addicted people who are employed are afraid to seek help through either private hospital-based treatment programs or their own physicians. David Smith and Donald Wesson (1988), suggest these people are wary of the risk that the diagnosis required by their insurance company would reveal their addiction to their employers. The result is many people seek treatment from alternative sources, including private practitioners, in order to avoid embarrassment or other problems related to employment security.

Finally, because of the tremendous increase in drug abuse[7], the treatment community is now faced with a crisis in treating chemically dependent clients. As an adjunct to any therapist's or clinician's arsenal of interventions, a solid understanding of the developmental processes of addiction, recovery and relapse prevention are becoming more and more important. The therapist treating addictive disorders must become conversant with recovery processes, self-help groups such as Alcoholics Anonymous, and the terminology associated with these organizations and processes, to both affirm (pace) the needs of their clients and positively reinforce (lead) their continuing recovery.

NOTES FOR INTRODUCTION

1. For an interesting and entertaining version of "the early days" in the development of NLP, I highly recommend Terry McClendon's book *The Wild Days: NLP 1972 - 1981.*

2. One of the interesting sidelights of this type of "setting oneself apart" has been the apparent belief that all which has been created *must be protected.* The originators of NLP registered that term, and for some time, it could not be used without their permission. My first book deleted that term from its original title, but it has since been changed to reflect its true contents to *Magic* of NLP *Demystified.* With the above forewarning, then, it is with the same caution that I follow the instructions from *Know How* and quote the following:

> *Mental Aptitude Patterning, MAP, EMPRINT, MAPP, and Future Pace are all protected marks owned by FuturePace, Inc. None of them may be used in connection with the sale, promotion, description, name, or advertisement of any person, product, or service whatsoever without the prior written consent of FuturePace, Inc. Critical essays, articles, or reviews that refer to any of these marks must also restate the first sentence of this paragraph....*

These authors who have gone to great lengths to differentiate what they do from what the NLPers do (which, as we shall see, is simply another form of cognitive behavioral therapy). As the reader will note, there are differences, but it is the similarities to which I am addressing this work.

3. Darling goes on to point out that, if their claims were true, "...NLP should be universally acknowledged as one of the century's greatest discoveries. In fact, it languishes in relative obscurity, largely ignored..." (p. 39). Her probing article attempts to defend the merits of NLP, especially when applied in the business and educational communities.

4. This book was written with John McInerney, Raymond DiGiuseppe and Raymond Yeager. If you've had the opportunity of listening to Albert Ellis speak either in person or on tape, you probably experienced his own very special rendition of this phenomenon of separation and aggrandizement!

5. Adhering to the bias I frequently encounter in literature in the field of addiction, I assume strong parallels between addiction, alcoholism, and other compulsive mood-altering activities. One enlightening discussion comes from Brownell, Marlatt, Lichtenstein, & Wilson (1986) who write: "Compelling arguments can be marshaled for both commonalties and differences in the addictive disorders" (p. 765). However, they point out that, based on the similarity of rates for relapse, there is increasing emphasis on commonalties.

6. In fact, Terrance Gorski (1989) writes (somewhat tongue-in-cheek), "It seems as if one of the conditions of being admitted to certain centers that treat celebrities is that the patients have a press conference on the second day of detox to announce that they are there" (p. 35).

7. This increase was spawned in part by the permissive attitudes of the 60s and 70s and by the introduction of more potent (cannabis is ten times more powerful today than it was in the 70's), more accessible (crack cocaine is a "merchandiser's dream") and more exotic (from *purple haze* to *ecstasy*) drugs.

NEURO-LINGUISTIC PROGRAMMING AS A COGNITIVE BEHAVIORAL THERAPY

...for there is nothing

either good or bad

but thinking makes it so...

–W. Shakespeare, *Hamlet*

During late 1973 and early 1974, I was introduced to the dramatic therapeutic techniques being developed by a small group of people in Santa Cruz, California. Having recently finished a stint with the military, I was looking for some direction in both my personal and professional life. I found it while working through various personal issues in the early NLP therapy groups in the Santa Cruz mountains and on Mission Street. Terry McClendon's book *The Wild Days* (1989) provides an entertaining look at those early days of NLP. Evolving from the therapeutic techniques of Fritz Perls, Virginia Satir, Milton Erickson and others, as interpreted by Richard Bandler, and shaped by the general semantics and linguistic models background of John Grinder, the field of neuro-linguistic programming was created in those early therapy groups.

In his introduction to *The Structure of Magic, Vol. I* (Bandler & Grinder, 1975), Gregory Bateson noted the authors utilized the field of linguistics to create both a theory of, and a tool for, therapy. By expanding on linguistics theory, Bateson observed, they had also made "...explicit the syntax of how people avoid change and, therefore, how to assist them in changing" (p. x).

During my self-exploration in those early sessions, as both client and student, I was exposed to a dynamic new therapy which focused on the *syntax* and *semantics* of human behavior. I found myself being finessed into more positive directions in my life. The "magic" of those early days experimenting with processes of therapeutic change eventually expanded into the field of NLP. Neuro-linguistic Programming is rooted in therapy. This book focuses on that application of NLP: the use of these powerful tools for positive therapeutic change.

NLP evolved within a larger theoretical and applied school of psychology that had also begun to come into its own at the same time. This chapter will focus primarily on the parallel development of cognitive behavioral therapy and neuro-linguistic programming. The material that follows is organized to show the relationship between NLP and the more widely accepted CBT.

CBT DEFINED

...the cognitive-behavioral therapies share a belief that therapeutic change can be effected through an alteration of idiosyncratic, dysfunctional modes of thinking (Keith Dobson and Lory Block, 1988, p. 29).

In seeking a comprehensive definition of CBT, I confronted the same problems one encounters when trying to define NLP. There is no simple definition that adequately encompasses either of these disciplines. I chose Dobson and Block (1988), because they have compiled a fairly representative analysis of CBT. They propose cognitive-behavioral therapies are actually a "...hybrid of behavioral strategies and cognitive processes with the goal of achieving behavioral and cognitive change" (p. 12).

Most writers in the field of CBT agree there are three basic assumptions which underlie all cognitive-behavioral therapies. The first is a person's cognitions (thinking, remembering, imagining) effect his or her behavior. The second assumption is these cognitive activities can be monitored by the individual performing them. The third is therapeutic changes in the person's behavior can be achieved through cognitive changes.

To summarize, CBT assumes a person's thoughts or beliefs (cognitions) affect his behavior, including both movement and emotion, and therapeutic interventions operate at the level of the client's models of the world (schemata, beliefs, or internal dialogue) to effect positive change. Central to the theory of change espoused by CBT theorists and clinicians, is the concept of a *mediational effect*. This concept hypothesizes that people's thoughts and beliefs effect their behaviors, including physical and physiological action as well as emotions. This is the cornerstone of CBT, and it is also one of the major connections between CBT and NLP.

NLP DEFINED

On the first page of their primary text in the field of NLP, the above authors describe the component pieces of the model. They begin with the idea all of our behaviors, including physical, visceral, thought and emotions, stem from neurological processes (*neuro*). These processes "...are represented, ordered and sequenced into models and strategies through language and communication systems..." (*linguistic*). Finally, *programming* is the process by which we organize and change the various components of the system.

Robert Dilts and Todd Epstein have recently created the "NLP University"[1]. In one of their brochures, I found one of the clearest definitions of NLP: "NLP is a pragmatic school of thought — an

The name neuro-linguistic programming stands for what we maintain to be the basic process used by all human beings to encode, transfer, guide, and modify behavior (Dilts, et. al., 1980, p. 1).

'epistemology' — that addresses the many levels involved in being human." They continue, NLP "...describes the fundamental dynamics between mind (neuro) and language (linguistic) and how their interplay effects our body and behavior (programming)."

As does a cognitive-behavioral therapist, an NLP practitioner works with a client to alter the interaction between his or her language (thoughts and beliefs) and behaviors, including emotions (neurology), through therapeutic interventions (intentional goal-directed programming).

SCHEMATIC OF THE TWO MODELS

Using the above descriptions, I created a visual representation of the basic components of these two therapeutic models. Remember, I am concentrating on the therapeutic applications of NLP in this work. There are many other applications of this discipline which lie outside the scope of this volume.

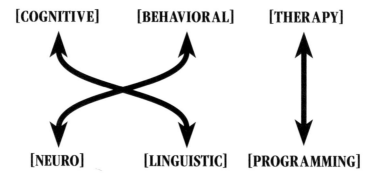

[COGNITIVE] [BEHAVIORAL] [THERAPY]

[NEURO] [LINGUISTIC] [PROGRAMMING]

The above comparison does not attempt to imply that CBT and NLP are one and the same. The point of the diagram is to show the strong similarities between cognitive-behavioral therapy and the therapeutic use of neuro-linguistic programming. As mentioned earlier, NLP has not been generally well-received by the established psychological community, while CBT has. Because CBT *has* received this general acceptance I believe the benefits of this metaphor warrant such an analogy be drawn. In later chapters, I will show how certain NLP techniques can assist the achievement of the therapeutic goals of the CBT therapist, while the abundant and well-documented research in the field of CBT can help substantiate the efficacy of NLP as a viable methodology in its own right.

THE ORIGINS OF CBT

One historian and a recognized founding father of CBT, Albert Ellis (1989), has proposed a relationship between CBT and early philosophers such as Confucius, Socrates and Epictetus. In his treatise on the origins of CBT, Ellis (1989) quotes the first century A.D. stoic, Epictetus, who wrote "People are disturbed not by things, but by the views which they take of them" (p. 6). He points out, however, it wasn't until the early 1940's that direct work with a person's belief systems was integrated into specific therapeutic processes.

Ellis notes that the early work of Gordon Alport and Prescott Lecky were the source for the idea that self-image is the result of a person's cognitions, and that changing these cognitions changes the self-concept. Their work established the foundation for the cognitive-behavioral movement. The awareness that we "build our own realities" has been with us for a long, long time.

Taking a somewhat different approach, Dobson and Block (1988), propose the cognitive-behavioral movement was actually the product of traditional behavioral therapy. They suggest it was encouraged by the need to explain the "black box", the term popularized during the behavioral movement, because behaviorists could not explain *how* certain internal processes worked. Because of pressure to address this problem, behaviorists began to accept the volumes of research showing evidence of cognitive factors in learning and other behaviors.

Most writers in the field point to the development and widespread popularity of Albert Ellis' rational- emotive therapy (RET) in the mid 1950's as the beginnings of modern cognitive behavioral therapy.[2] There have been many other contributions by a host of theorists, researchers and therapists. According to one source, however, the key components of CBT did not gain the popular respect of mainstream psychology until the late 1960's and early 1970's (Kazdin, 1978).

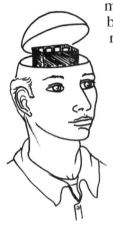

Regardless of the position historians take as to the origins of CBT, they agree the single most important factor in the acceptance of CBT was the development of the hypothesis of a *mediational effect*. This is the effect a person's internal cognitive processes has on his or her behavior and learning. It is this concept, more than anything else, which differentiates CBT from the behavioral therapies. According to Dobson and Block (1988), this transformation occurred in the late 1960's and early 1970's and was the result of six important factors.

THE BLACK BOX

First, these authors suggest the traditional approaches to therapy, especially the behavioral school, were unable to describe adequately all human behavior. For example, Albert Bandura's (1965) work on vicarious learning could not be explained by the behaviorists, who rigidly refused to entertain the notion of unobservable cognitive processes (popularly labeled the "black box"). Second, there was a growing dissatisfaction with the psychoanalytic point of view. Third, there was concern the popular behavioral approaches were essentially ignoring significant problem areas. Fourth, as the field of cognitive psychology continued to grow, there was increasing support for research being done on the mediational models. Fifth, the authors propose that the increasing excitement and public declaration by many respected psychologists who were embracing this new field was creating a *zeitgeist* which brought even more attention to the field. Finally, say Dobson and Block, there was the continued publication of studies which "...found treatment outcomes for cognitive-behavioral treatments equally or more effective than strictly behavioral approaches" (p. 10).

THE ORIGINS OF NLP

NLP's roots start in the general area of Santa Cruz, California, during the early 1970's. A student of Fritz Perls' Gestalt Therapy, Richard Bandler brought to the original team of Bandler and Grinder certain biases which formed the foundation of what we now know as NLP. Gestalt psychologists varied from the behaviorists in their emphasis on the importance of patterns of perceptual experience. In the last book published by Perls (1973 – edited by Bandler), he proposes that "...it is the organization of facts, perceptions, behavior or phenomena...that defines them and gives them their specific and particular meaning" (p. 2). This emphasis on *patterns* of behavior and experience became a cornerstone of NLP.

Perls also describes what he terms the "holistic doctrine" as a counter to the older "psycho-physical parallelism." This newer approach to understanding behavior suggests that the relationship between the mind and body is inseparable. After describing various thinking and imagining processes, Perls states, "In all these mental activities, the relationship between what we do and what we think is very clear. When we are aware of something, or focus attention on it, or attempt to exert our will on it, *there are at least some overt signs by which the spectator can see that these processes are at work*" (p. 11, emphasis added).[3] As a Gestalt trainer, Bandler was acutely alert to the minute changes in clients' behaviors. He utilized this information during therapy/training sessions to enhance his effectiveness. This emphasis on observing subtle behaviors, combined with the Gestalt orientation to the psychophysical field, with its corollary concept of isomorphism[4], were likely influences in the later development of NLP's *representational systems*. These perceptual patterns are fully described in Grinder and Bandler, 1976; and Lewis and Pucelik, 1982. Additional information is included in Appendix 2 of this book.

Gregory Bateson also played a significant role in the development of NLP. An early mentor and colleague of John Grinder's at UCSC, Bateson's influence can be seen in several areas. Bateson is often quoted in the early works of Bandler and Grinder, and he wrote the introduction to their first book. Of course, Grinder, also a linguist by training, brought his own biases into play. This is especially clear in the first Bandler and Grinder book, *The Structure of Magic, Vol. I*, a treatise on the structure of the language of therapeutic change. As an undergraduate student at UCSC, I studied under Dr. Grinder, exploring many of the ideas which were included in the early NLP publications.

NLP AS A CBT

In his review of the development of CBT, Ellis (1989) states that between 1975 and 1979, there was a rapid acceleration in cognitive-behavioral research and applications. Because so many theorists and researchers were embracing this new psychology, it could no longer be ignored. He writes, "So many significant texts on RET and CBT were...published that it is difficult to list even the most outstanding ones. Some of the influential ones included those by Bandler and Grinder..." (p. 12). This reference to NLP by one of the paragons of the CBT movement is significant because it associates Bandler and Grinder with other prominent writers in the field of CBT, including Bandura, Beck, Ellis, Haley, and Meichenbaum.

Why did Ellis choose to place NLP on his list of influential texts in the field of CBT? What did he see in Bandler and Grinder's work that demonstrated such a relationship? One of the most striking similarities between CBT and NLP is the use of an information-processing model. In his foreword to the *Comprehensive Handbook of Cognitive Therapy*, Marvin Goldfried (1989) describes the CBT paradigm to include "...several nonconscious cognitive processes that operate both on incoming and stored information" (p. x). These processes are clearly defined by early NLP writers (Bandler and Grinder, 1975; Lewis and Pucelik, 1982) as "generalization, deletion and distortion: the universal human modeling processes."

There are quite a number of current approaches to therapy which fall within the scope of CBT as it has been defined. The common element of these therapies is a theoretical perspective which assumes internal covert processes called thinking or cognition occur, and these cognitive processes mediate changes in a person's behavior. One remarkable aspect of NLP is that it attempts to make these covert processes overt and, therefore, observable. Such tools as *minimal cues* and *accessing cues*[5] assist the NLP practitioner in identifying and mapping "covert" processes. Such information can greatly expedite any therapist's work, regardless of his or her theoretical school or biases.

According to Mahoney and Arnkoff (1978), CBTs can be sorted into three major classes. These classes are differentiated from each other based on their primary goals for therapeutic change. The three classes are cognitive-restructuring therapies, coping-skills therapies and problem-solving therapies[6].

Therapists who utilize *cognitive-restructuring* techniques perceive the problem needing treatment arising from within the client. Because the problems, depression, anxiety, emotional distress, etc. are believed to be the result of the client's own maladaptive thought processes, the intervention focuses on providing the client with alternative thinking strategies which are more likely to create positive results. This is similar to basic strategies work of in NLP. Working with the client, the NLP practitioner defines maladaptive sequences of thought (cognitions) and replaces certain sequences with more productive alternatives. Both CBT and NLP cognitive restructuring techniques are described in later chapters.

Coping-skills therapies, on the other hand, are useful when a problem is seen as a result of the client's responses to external circumstances. The therapist assists the client to develop new skills to cope with the particular stressful events or situations. These skills may include changing thoughts which exacerbate the problem, identifying new patterns of thought which will lessen the impact of the circumstances, and adopting new behaviors which will alleviate or lessen the consequences of the external problem. NLP's "10 minute phobia cure" is an example of this type of intervention. The work with belief systems described in later chapters exemplifies coping-skills therapy.

A blend of both coping-skills and cognitive-restructuring techniques, *problem-solving therapies* attempts to provide the client with techniques for dealing with either internally-generated or external problems. It also requires a close working relationship between the client and therapist to develop appropriate treatment strategies for the desired goals. Again, in the work of an NLP practitioner, similar interventions are used. For example, during the process of identifying a goal state with the client, the practitioner will insure that it is congruent and aligned with all parts and may use an NLP technique such as six-step reframing or dissociated state therapy.

In it's basic therapeutic applications, NLP emulates all three categories of cognitive behavioral therapy. With the abundance of research and application of these therapies, it seems a shame to persist in maintaining the myth of separation of NLP from all the other behavioral sciences. By sharing the theoretical constructs, the diversity of application and the wealth of research, the union of NLP with CBT will be mutually beneficial to each discipline.

INTERNAL DIALOGUE

One of the problems encountered by a new idea in the field of psychology is the difficulty assimilating it into the established mode of thought. The behaviorist movement of the 1920's and 1930's was a response to the demand to "harden" the field of psychology, in order to give it more credibility as a science. To the extent that behaviorism forced a more systematic exploration of complex behaviors, that goal was met. However, behaviorism failed to describe the more subtle and complex *internal* workings of the mind. Then general semanticists and early cognitivists began to propose alternative ways of explaining these unseen processes. They also made efforts to maintain an air of "hard science" in their descriptions while avoiding the "parlor science" of Freudian physics or the spiritualism of Jung.

The net result of these changes was the synthesis of a new school of thought. Meichenbaum (1977) may have documented this shift better than any other writer of the period. In his book, *Cognitive Behavior Modification*, he writes, "For the last ten years I have been attempting to bridge the gap between the clinical concerns of cognitive-semantic therapists (e.g., George Kelley, Jerome Frank, Albert Ellis, Aaron Beck, and Jerome L. Singer) and the technology of behavior therapy" (p. 11). His book is a "progress report" of research and treatment which demonstrate evidence of newly identified cognitive factors in the processes of behavior modification.

Meichenbaum identified the primary cognitive factor involved in the modification of behaviors. He called this construct *internal dialogue*, and noted, "Attributions, appraisals, interpretations, self-reinforcements, beliefs, defense mechanisms, and many other constructs, all have been offered to explain private conscious events or what I will refer to as "internal dialogue" (p. 12). He clarifies what we commonly refer to as "inner speech" as only one aspect of this construct.

The focus on internal processes and the exceptional ways in which they can be altered for therapeutic change has been one of the major contributions of NLP to the field of psychotherapy. Methods used by NLP practitioners to intervene with clients operate on what NLP labels the client's *strategies*. This cognitive construct is similar to what Meichenbaum calls internal dialogue. Like internal dialogue, strategies affect a person's behaviors. However, in addition to the attributes described by Meichenbaum, NLP strategies emphasize the use of *representational systems* as the basic building blocks of a person's strategies. Representational systems are the ways humans perceive, store and think about (represent) their experiences in the world. They include visual stimuli (both remembered images and constructed images), kinesthetic experiences (including visceral, emotional, proprioceptive, and sensational stimuli), auditory stimuli (experiences ranging from self-talk to tonal shifts to remembered and constructed dialogues, conversations, slogans, etc.), and olfactory/gustatory experiences (taste and smell). These are coded in the brain in specific patterns which become our *models* of the world. They form the strategies or *maps* which guide our behaviors and mold our perceptions. Like the other CBT constructs of complex internal processes, these representations of experience can be identified and altered to obtain therapeutic change in our clients.

In 1977, Meichenbaum wrote, "...research on cognitive factors in behavior therapy procedures has also indicated that what a person says to himself, that is, how he evaluates and interprets events, is explicitly modifiable by many of the behavior therapy techniques that have been used to modify maladaptive overt behaviors" (p. 108). This assumption is the fundamental link between the different CBTs. We can impact our clients through any of the different constructs discussed above (internal dialog, representational systems, beliefs, schemata, etc.) to effect positive therapeutic change. This is also the thread that ties NLP to CBT. The balance of this book will describe these constructs and how they can be applied by therapists towards this end.

NOTES FOR CHAPTER 1

1. NLP University: for more information, contact Robert Dilts and Todd Epstein at Dynamic Learning Center, Box 1112, Ben Lomond, CA 95005. Phone: (408) 336-3457.

2. Ellis (1989), himself claims this distinction, noting his interest in sex therapy, which he calls a "...special school of therapy that has always been cognitive-behavioral" (p.9).

3. He gives the following examples: "The man who is concentrating hard on what someone else is saying is likely to be sitting forward in his chair; his whole being seems to be aimed and directed towards that in which he is interested. The man who makes up his mind not to take that fifth piece of candy is likely to make a motion towards it, and to stop his hand suddenly and withdraw it before it reaches the candy dish" (p. 11).

4. As defined by Nordby and Hall (1974), "Isomorphism is Gestalt psychology's answer to the mind-body problem. Form and order in experience corresponds to (is isomorphous with) form and order in the physical world, and form and order in the physiological processes" (p. 61).

5. See Appendix 2 for a description of these NLP terms.

6. Dobson and Block (1988) identified the major cognitive-behavioral therapies. As listed below, the date shown is the year the therapy was first published and its primary authors' names follow. (Adapted from table 1.1, p. 12.)

> Coping-Skills therapies:
>> -Anxiety-Management Training (1971)
>> Suinn & Richardson
>>
>> -Stress Inoculation Training (1973)
>> Meichenbaum
>>
>> -Systematic Rational Restructuring (1974)
>> Goldfried
>
> Cognitive restructuring:
>> -RET (1962)
>> Ellis
>>
>> -Cognitive Therapy (1963)
>> Beck

-Self-Instructional Training (1971)
Meichenbaum

-RBT (1975)
Maultsby

-Structured Psychotherapy (1983)
Guido & Liotti

Problem-solving therapies:

-Problem-solving Therapy (1971)
D'Zurilla & Goldfried and Spivack & Shure

-Personal Science (1974)
Mahoney

-Self-control Therapy (1977)
Rehm

As noted in the text, NLP falls easily into all three major categories of CBT.

THE EMERGENT PARADIGM

The construction of our

models of the world is not a

haphazard, disorganized process.

It is a highly efficient, ongoing procedure

that operates throughout our whole lifetime

(Byron Lewis & Frank Pucelik, 1982, p. 17).

In late 1985 I started working in a small U.S. Army counseling center in central Europe. On my first day on the job, I was handed a stack of case files to review. Thumbing through these files filled with myriad abbreviations and Army "shorthand," I was struck by one central point: there appeared to be no organizing theme or structure to the counseling process. There was a haphazard attempt to address the identified problem, which was either "alcohol abuse" or "drug abuse," using something labeled "reality therapy." What was actually going on during the counseling sessions we later jokingly referred to as "talk-o-therapy." Of course, this needs to be distinguished from "walk-o-therapy," a technique that was required when our offices were demolished by a team of frenetic hammer and chisel-wielding workers to make way for a new family center, resulting in our relocation to an abandoned warehouse with no walls in which to provide our "private and confidential counseling." But that is another story completely!

This isn't to say there weren't some very professional, genuinely interested and concerned counselors working there. The Army was even providing some excellent training for counselors of alcohol and other drug abusing soldiers, civilian employees, and their family members. The problem was the lack of an underlying or unifying theme within the treatment. In retrospect, however, this problem seems to have simply been a reflection of the state of the field of addictions counseling at that time.

Prior to the 1980's there was no unified field of chemical dependency. There were, instead, a number of independent descriptions or theories of addiction, its treatment and the causes of relapse. Each approach had its adherents (many as outspoken as the founding NLPers!), but the differences between them were confusing and often contradictory. As a new professional in the field, I found the whole thing somewhat overwhelming. Where should I start in learning this new field and how could I apply my own background and training to this new counseling experience?

CONFUSION IN THE FIELD

Without the conceptual framework, unitary set of rules, or standards of practice provided by a paradigm, it has been difficult to agree on the important parameters of addictive behaviors
(Dennis Donovan, 1988, pp. 11-12).

It was nearly a century and a half ago that Magnus Huss coined the term "alcoholism". As I began combing through the literature in the field of addictions, I was struck by how much our understanding of this disorder has changed in the intervening years. I also discovered, as I become more familiar with the various perceptions and beliefs surrounding alcoholism and addiction, it was easier to understand the tremendous confusion confronting treatment providers in the field of addictions.

Writers and researchers in the field of alcoholism and addiction have been cognizant of the lack of any centralized theories for some time. In his review of the literature on alcoholism and addiction, George Jacobson (1989) noted a disconcerting fact. It seems that the very widely read E. M. Jellinek in his influential publication, *The Disease Concept of Alcoholism*, "...cited more that 200 definitions, conceptualizations, and theories of the etiology and treatment of alcoholism" (p. 18). And that was in 1960![1]

The abundance of theories created a competitive stance between the various schools of thought and approaches to treatment of addictive disorders. Each school attempted to achieve a dominant status, and for good reason. Only programs recognized by the establishment receive grants and other funding, and generally only those with such financial support are able to attract clients and staff to their specific treatment programs.

With all this competition to attract funding, it makes sense that there was confusion in the field. I have some good news, however. During the last decade this "mess" has begun to change. The change to a more eclectic view of addiction is being reflected by much of the recent literature.[2]

MODELS OF ADDICTION

There are several reasons for including a review of theoretical approaches to addiction. As pointed out, such a review will help the reader understand how the field became so confusing. There are other important reasons for therapists working in the field to have an overview of the major theories of addiction.

Although guided by specific operational principles when working with clients, therapists are also greatly influenced by their own beliefs about alcoholism and drug addiction. Our own biases have

How we call a thing, the name we give it, influences our reactions to it, our perceptions of it, our feelings and attitudes toward it (George Jacobson, 1989, p. 19).

considerable impact on both the approaches we choose and the outcome of the therapeutic intervention. Robert Dilts (1990-a, 1990-b) warns us to be wary of what he calls the "fish in the dreams" phenomenon. This is where the therapist constructs evidence of beliefs, strategies, etc. in the client based on the therapist's own projections rather than what the client presents. The confusing array of theories and beliefs available to the therapists today make it critical that we become conscious of our own biases and have available the requisite variety to avoid "putting fish in our clients' dreams."

FISHING

During the years I have been working in this field, the best therapists and the best Twelve Step sponsors I have met have been guided by one primary axiom: The more you know about the problem, the more effective you can be. Knowledge is an important ingredient in *requisite variety*. Borrowed from systems theory, requisite variety is the principle that the element with the most flexibility in a system will have the most control over the system. The better informed the therapist is, the more likely he/she will be able to effectively work with the alcoholic, drug addicted or compulsive client. In addition, knowledge of these models can be extremely useful in building therapeutic metaphors, and as rational scientific information for disputing client's irrational beliefs. For clients also, knowledge provides more control. The more informed the client, the more choices he or she will have.

The changes in the field of addiction treatment have been rapid in the last few years, and there is growing support for what Donovan (1988) calls the *emergent view* described at the end of this chapter. What follows is a partial list of some of the more influential models and theories of alcoholism, addiction, and relapse which have contributed to the emergent paradigm gaining wide acceptance in the field today. I invite the reader to identify, as we go along, which of these positions or schools of thought you lean towards yourself.

Finally, theory always guides research, and treatment trends are influenced by the results of research. The following brief survey of the more influential theories will help us understand why the research has taken many different, and sometimes conflicting paths, resulting in confusion among the treatment community.

MORALITY VERSUS THE DRUG ISSUE

Confusion about the problems associated with alcohol abuse probably dates to the origins of wine itself. In times past, abusive drinking was assumed to be a personal choice, something ultimately within the control of the drinker. The alcoholic, was viewed as a sinner. The word "spirits" used to describe distilled alcohol are a reference to an archaic concept of demonic "possession" by the drinker. Even as recently as the turn of the century, alcohol abuse was seen primarily as a moral issue or a "disease of the spirit."

The degree to which this moralistic point of view continues to affect us can be seen in our legal system. As pointed out by Fingarette (1988), alcoholism is widely accepted now as a *primary disease* (see the following section) whose acquisition lies outside the control of the alcoholic. However, law (our codified moral standards) holds an individual accountable for his actions under the influence, *even if he is medically diagnosed as an alcoholic*. In other words, he will be punished for something that medical science says is outside his control — the disease of alcoholism — based on moral judgements: the law.

During the final decades of the last century and preceding the prohibition era, a new approach to the problem of drunkenness swept the country. Unlike the moralists, the temperance movement emphasized the dangers of the drug alcohol over the morality of the drinker. This was an important shift in emphasis. The movement was popular until the repeal of Prohibition in 1933 and helped pave the way for the view of alcoholism as a disease. The organization frequently used reformed problem drinkers to talk with others and warn them of the inherent risks of drinking and dangers of alcohol. A modified version of this same technique was used by the later movement of Alcoholics Anonymous.

BACCUS – GREEK GOD OF WINE

THE AMERICAN DISEASE MODEL

G. Alan Marlatt (1985) also addressed the moral issue, observing that more recent models of alcoholism may actually facilitate recovery. He wrote, "By attempting to remove the moral stigma associated with drinking problems, the diagnosis of alcoholism as a disease encourages many individuals to seek medical treatment for their disorder" (p. 6). The underlying theme of the American Disease Model of alcoholism can be traced back to the early nineteenth century writings of the American Physician, Benjamin Rush. However, it was the work of Jellinek (1952, 1960) and his associates at the Yale Center for Alcohol Studies that popularized the modern version.

Fingarette (1988), however, points out that, although it is the single most popularly accepted view of alcoholism, few people, even those working in the field, can recite the disease theory of alcoholism. His definition of the disease model of alcoholism (pp. 2-3) contains the following components:

- It is a specific disease to which only some people are vulnerable.
- The disease will develop if someone who is vulnerable takes up drinking.
- The disease is progressive: it starts with social drinking and progresses to heavy drinking, drinking alone or in secret, ultimately leads to the development of tolerance with physical withdrawal symptoms upon cessation of the drinking.
- The drinker begins to experience blackouts and other symptoms of heavy use.
- The alcoholic finally succumbs to uncontrolled use.
- The alcoholic "hits bottom" and suffers physical or emotional collapse and premature death.
- The only other alternative is life-long abstention.

This model of alcoholism has been widely applied to other addictions as well. The model posits that addiction is a progressive disease which advances through fairly standard stages regardless of the user's background or any other individual characteristics. Ultimately, the addict will "hit bottom", enter a crisis situation, and seek help for the problem. If help is not sought, the addict faces physical and/or emotional collapse with premature death the only other endpoint. According to the proponents of this model, there is only one approach to treatment. Regardless of how it is achieved, the addict must ultimately abstain for life, because the disease is seen as incurable.

ALCOHOLICS ANONYMOUS

Although it wasn't until 1956 that the American Medical Association officially recognized alcoholism as a primary disease, there were a number of factors leading to this event. Prior to the founding of Alchoholics Anonymous (AA) in 1935, the traditional treatment for alcoholics was to hospitalize them. Chronic relapsers were given little hope of recovery, and it was generally believed that the affliction was progressive and fatal.

Following directly on the heels of the repeal of the 18th Amendment which ended prohibition, two men sought to popularize a new approach to the previously untreatable chronic alcoholics. Based in large part on principles from a Christian-oriented movement called the Oxford Group, Bill W. and Bob S. initiated a program of "one drunk talking to another" as a means of keeping themselves sober. Although slow to catch on, AA and the other Twelve Step programs (Narcotics Anonymous, Cocaine Anonymous, Gamblers Anonymous, etc.) have become the most influential and widespread "treatment" of alcoholics, addicts, and other compulsive disorders in the United States.

Building on the disease model of addiction, the basic premise of the founders of AA is that alcoholics are physiologically different from normal drinkers. They have an inherent inability to drink "socially" due to their disease thought of as an "allergy". As W. D. Silkworth wrote, "We believe...that the action of alcohol on those chronic alcoholics is a manifestation of an allergy; that the phenomenon of craving is limited to this class and never occurs in the average temperate drinker." [3]

Finding support from the medical community through such notable physicians as Dr. Silkworth, and later from Dr. Jellinek, AA popularized what became known as the American Disease Model of alcoholism. Like the temperance movement, this model de-emphasized the judgmental moral approach to alcoholism requiring punishment and/or incarceration (either in prisons or sanitariums). However, instead of focusing on the drug (alcohol), AA oriented its adherents toward the primary symptoms of the disease, the physical, psychological, social and spiritual problems that result from chronic alcohol abuse.

One of the positive results of this model is that it deals with the tremendous guilt associated with addiction. Jampolski (1991) writes, "In the early recovery, the disease concept allows the individual and family to let go of some blame, condemnation, judgement, and guilt" (p. 15). He warns, however, that this same concept can also be used to provide the alcoholic with an excuse to "shuck responsibility." Here is an excellent example of how being alert to our clients' beliefs about their problem can help the counselor provide the best possible interventions while preventing their sabotaging the recovery efforts.

The medical model prescribes specific action for intervention in cases of addiction. Once identified, the individual with the disease must be convinced that he/she has a life-threatening condition. Then the individual must be persuaded to quit using and remain abstinent permanently. Twelve Step programs, such as Alcoholics Anonymous, are extremely effective at accomplishing this end. During meetings, newcomers are shown how the disease progresses through the stories, often referred to as "drunkologues," of other individuals in recovery. They are encouraged to relate their own experiences to others in the meetings, breaking down their isolation and feelings of being different. The "Big Book" reinforces the idea that continued drinking or using ultimately ends in death. The "fellowship" of those in recovery is a built-in support system for each individual, and "membership" in this abstinent community is seen as a life-long commitment. I will go into greater detail on Twelve Step Programs in Chapter 4.

The AA model suggests that addiction is the result of psychological or biological preconditions inherent in an individual. Moreover, these are conditions over which he or she has no control. This eliminates the guilt associated with the moral concept of lost will power, and focuses away from the drug or the alcohol. Finally, life-long abstinence is seen as the only cure.

PSYCHOANALYTIC MODELS

Psychoanalysts have long sought to define or at least describe the basic makeup of the *alcoholic personality*. The search has been for specific "abnormalities of personality" in an effort to explain addiction. Fixations, unresolved early conflicts, arrested development (i.e., stuck at the "oral stage") are some of the explanations used by the psychoanalytic school to define the origins of the condition.

At the extreme end of the psychoanalytic school are theories that addiction is the result of latent homosexuality, of sex-role conflicts, or deep-seated drives for power and control originating from a sense of impotence. From this standpoint, therefore, intervention necessitates a long-term commitment to psychoanalysis. This costly and time consuming process has had only limited success with the addicted client.

One fairly recent approach coming from the Harvard Cocaine Recovery Project shows some promise. Called "Modified Dynamic Group Therapy" or MDGT

(Khantzian, Halliday, & McAuliffe, 1990), the originators state, "It is designed to treat substance abuse by
ultimately focusing on the long-standing problems of
character and personality that are thought to lead to
drug use" (p. xi). Utilizing a group format that meets
twice weekly for six
months, the process
seeks to address the
client's sense of vul-
nerability, to teach
him or her the
value of attachment
and to provide in-
struction in the
area of self-care.

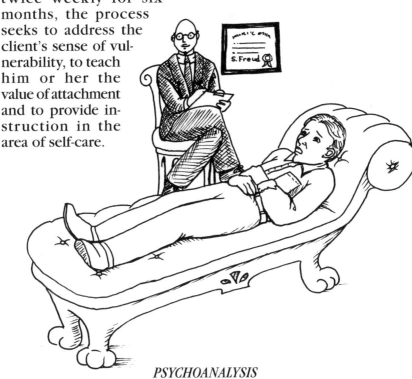

PSYCHOANALYSIS

In describing their rationale for using groups in treating addiction, the authors write, "Groups are powerful
ways of addressing and modifying the vulnerabilities
that lie at the heart of psychological suffering and compulsive drug use. Groups have the capacity, when
well-led, to improve self-care, to oppose the forces of
shame and isolation, to evoke the expression of individual character style, and to enlarge and enliven the
person's view of self and capacity for choice" (p. xvi).[4]
Here, again, we have shame and isolation being dealt
with as well as basic self-esteem and self-care.

THE BEHAVIORAL MODEL

The primary effect of the initial drug doses or other compulsive behaviors (gambling, sex, shopping) – the sense of euphoria, well-being, relaxation or excitement – is seen by the behavioral school as a primary cause of addiction. Behaviorism suggests that any rewarded behavior is likely to be repeated, especially if it is regularly *reinforced* by repeated rewards. The potent rewarding effect of drug use makes it likely that an individual will be motivated to repeat the behavior. In behavioral terms, this is called *operant conditioning*.

Research strongly supports behaviorists' contention that stimulus-response learning theory has a direct bearing on early drinking. In addition, behavioral researchers have demonstrated how classical conditioning can be used to describe aspects of tolerance. Obviously, there are certain drugs that have stronger *reinforcing attributes* than others. Washington (1989), for example, talks about the "pharmacologic imperative" of cocaine. Drawing from the work of Dr. Sidney Cohen, Washington observes how "...the powerfully rewarding properties of cocaine [are] capable of making obsessive users of even the most mature and well-integrated persons among us" (p.13).

One of the most well-known treatment interventions for alcoholism using strict behavioral interventions is *aversion therapy*. This form of treatment involves giving the patient an emetic such as disulfiram (Antabuse) prior to drinking, then giving the patient his or her favorite drink. The technique was introduced in the early 1940's, according to Wolpe (1969). He notes that this procedure is repeated for seven to ten days and observes, "If there is sufficient conditioning the very sight of alcohol will produce nausea" (p. 209).

BIOLOGICAL MODELS

There are actually several different models that have evolved from research on biological aspects of addiction. The first, and most well known, is the *genetic* model. This theory proposes that the genesis of addiction stems from a genetic predisposition. Certain individuals contain an inherited physiology that makes them more susceptible to the addictive effects of drugs and alcohol than the general populace.

In other research, the primary focus has been on a *metabolism and brain chemistry* model involving tetrahydroisoquinolines (TIQ). In simple terms, the TIQ hypothesis proposes that during the metabolism of alcohol, the brains of alcoholics produce chemical by-products with opiate-like properties, and this is what the alcoholic becomes addicted to (Blum and Payne, 1991).

Another biological model that is derived from both of the above models supports a *psychogenetic* theory of alcoholism (Blum and Payne, 1991). Based on the discovery that all alcoholics are deficient in the synthesis and regulation of natural opioids in the brain, this theory posits three types of alcoholics: 1) those born with genetic deficiencies of internal opioids, 2) those with stress-induced deficiencies of internal opioids, and 3) those whose drinking causes alcohol-induced deficiencies of internal opioids.

In the first type of alcoholic, the person is born with a genetic defect in the production and regulation of certain chemicals in the brain. This creates a natural "craving" for alcohol in order to stimulate production of the under-produced chemicals. Of course, this process won't occur unless the person starts drinking and discovers that he or she suddenly "feels normal". The second type of alcoholism results from prolonged stress which reduces the individual's ability to regulate these brain chemicals. The last alcoholic is one who has "practiced" his or her way into the disease by drinking a sufficient amount and regularly enough to cause damage to the brain's ability to produce these chemicals naturally.

Originating from genetics research during the 1960s and 1970s, the biological models began to take focus in the 1970s by showing connections between the acquisition of the disease and hereditary and biochemical factors. There are several important implications for intervention based on these models: if alcoholism is genetically inherited, abstention will be mandated. If it arises from a TIQ etiology, counseling towards moderation to avoid the effects that cause the chemical changes would be warranted. If it is stress-induced, early detection and treatment of the stressors would be critical in treatment.

SOCIAL LEARNING THEORY MODEL

Based in large part on the work of Bandura, many social learning theorists propose that addiction is learned behavior.[5] While not discounting the potential effects of genetic predisposition or other factors, social learning researchers see alcohol and drug abuse which leads to addiction as a failure in the client's learning certain *discriminatory functions*. What this means is that the individual is unable to discern what is appropriate and productive behavior related to drinking and using.

One of the primary ways loss of discrimination occurs is through the client's *modeling* behaviors. For any number of reasons, an individual will copy the drinking or drug use patterns of influential people (family members, peers, media personalities). Because of the pressure to "drink like a man" or smoke "Brand X" to be cool, the person continues to imbibe or use well past what feels right or healthy. The result after repeated abuse is the loss of the ability to respond appropriately to changes in his/her own internal and external environments.

Social learning theorists also propose that the addict uses, drinks, gambles, etc. as a means of *coping* with problems. Using modeling and coping skills to explain the complex interactions between an addict and his/her environment, social learning theorists expanded on the purely behavioral determinants of addiction and alcoholism. Included within their research are certain cognitive processes, especially *positive expectancies*. These are beliefs that alcohol or drugs cause desirable effects: "They help me relax," or, "They help me cope." Such beliefs promote heavier and more frequent drinking or using. As we shall see in Chapters 5, 6, and 7, knowing and working with the client's beliefs are a critical aspect of the therapeutic process.

Two major themes of treatment from a social learning point of view are changing the client's perceptions and changing the environment. The first requires the use of techniques such as *cognitive restructuring* (described in Chapter 5) to change a client's positive expectancies or beliefs about tension

SOCIAL PRESSURE

reduction and other desirable effects of alcohol or drugs. The second requires clients to learn new coping skills and encourages environmental changes. Clients need to change their friends (especially heavy drinking/using role models) and stop going to places where they might be influenced to return to use (bars, night clubs, etc.).

COGNITIVE BEHAVIORAL MODELS

Cognitive models became popular in the early 1960s as the result of therapists and researchers such as Albert Ellis and Aaron Beck. Jacqueline Pearsons (1989) points out that cognitive-behavioral therapists generally assume the client's problem occurs at two levels. The first is the overt difficulty, such as depression or drug addiction. The second involves underlying psychological mechanisms, psychological deficits or distortions, usually *irrational beliefs*, that cause the problem.

It is important to understand the major premise of cognitive approaches to treatment: the dysfunction originates within what cognitive behaviorists call the client's *schemata*. This is a person's *core belief system*. While not negating the potential influences of other factors, such as genetic predisposition or biochemical imbalances, the focus of cognitive approaches is on how the client maintains painful, harmful, or irrational behaviors. Because the CBT therapist works on clients' belief systems through their internal and external language, the primary treatment approaches utilize some form of *debate*. This involves pointing out to clients the irrationality of certain core beliefs and the construction and rehearsing of rational self-statements or other more functional cognitive strategies and skills.

The similarities between CBT and NLP were delineated in the last chapter. The debate process when utilized by an NLP practitioner does not necessarily need to occur at a conscious level nor is it limited to linguistic interventions. A skilled practitioner can elicit, map, and facilitate changes in the person's strategies and belief systems using other cognitive functions as we shall see in later chapters.

THE DAMAGED BRAIN MODEL

Primary proponents of what is also known as the *neurological impairment* model are Gorski and Miller (1982, 1986). Beginning with the fact that chronic, long-term alcohol and drug abuse results in damage to cells that make up the brain, spinal column and peripheral nerves, this model of addiction demonstrates how such neurological damage effects the individual psychologically and socially as well.

Over time, an individual adapts to increasing levels of intoxication or drug use. Eventually, he or she comes to depend upon the drug to simply feel OK (maintain homeostasis). The intoxicating effects of the drug increasingly impair the person's ability to cope psychologically with the myriad of life's stresses, and the individual's social life progressively centers more and more around the acquisition, use, and recovery from the drug. Gorski and Miller adopted the *biopsychosocial* model of disease from medical science. Using this model, they propose that relapse is simply the result of dysfunction in one or more of those three areas of functioning resulting in the addict or alcoholic attempting to regain homeostasis through a return to use.

One important aspect of this model to the therapist is the assumption that when you are working with a chronic drug or alcohol abuser, you are working with a damaged brain. Gorski and Miller delineate several major categories of mental dysfunction. First, there is difficulty in thinking clearly. This includes a very brief attention span, rigid, concrete thinking patterns, an inability to abstract or perceive cause-effect relationships, and the inability to solve simple problems. What this means to the therapist, for example, is that there may be problems eliciting and installing what would normally be fairly simple strategies. The client may become easily confused, may inadvertently block the process with rigid/repetitive thoughts not easily extinguished, and have difficulty in following even the most simple instructions during the therapeutic process.

In addition, both short and long-term memory are affected. This could result in a set of instructions, a new belief, or a newly installed strategy failing to make the necessary neurological leap from short to long term areas of brain functioning. This may prevent a new strategy or skill from gaining a foothold and can prevent the natural process of generalization to other similar problem areas.

These problems might be confounding to the therapist or NLP practitioner operating from the assumption (based of course on previous successes installing new strategies in "normal" clients) that the session is complete once the final "check" has been made following the intervention. In addition, when reconstructing past strategies, especially when asking for remembered material from early experiences, the client may simply "draw a blank" that is (at least for the moment) immune to even the most artistic interventions.

Gorski and Miller's research with alcoholics supports their contention that this dysfunction at the neurological level will impact the client's ability to sleep restfully, to handle stress, to manage their emotions and can lead to dizziness and loss of coordination with a tendency to become accident prone. To the therapist not already experienced with recovering addicts and alcoholics, this may present a confusing array of apparently untreatable symptoms. However, as the research shows, these symptoms are often temporary, appear to be compounded by stress, and can be overcome. However, this will take time (6 to 18 months for the early symptoms of the disorder--the post acute withdrawal symptoms — to diminish) and will require patience of the therapist and a willingness to repeatedly install disrupted strategies or reconstruct new belief statements regularly over the course of treatment.[6]

MULTIDIMENSIONAL CRAVINGS MODEL

Moving in the direction of a more comprehensive view of addiction, another team of researchers has proposed a *psychobiological* model to explain the phenomena of craving. Describing it as "multidimensional" in nature (craving includes cognitive, behavioral, physiological and neurophysiological components), Ludwig, Wikler, and Stark (1974) suggest that craving is a *conditioned cognitive label* that has become associated with the discomfort of withdrawal (neurological and physiological processes) and with negative mood states (like depression, anxiety, loneliness, or boredom) often associated with withdrawal.

Using behavioral terminology (i.e., classical conditioning), this model theorizes that an alcoholic experiences negative mood states or sensations, especially during withdrawal. Since alcoholics know that drinking will reduce those feelings and improve their mood, they link thoughts of drinking or using to those specific negative sensations and then give them the cognitive label "craving." After repeated pairings of the sensations with the thoughts, eventually the alcoholic or addict will "have a craving" anytime he or she feels uncomfortable or stressed, and drinking or using then becomes an instrumental response (well anchored) that will reduce the negative arousal state. These researchers underscore the importance of cognitive processes in the alcoholic's experience of "craving." They point out that craving does not necessarily lead to drinking and that drinking does not necessarily lead to loss of control. Loss of control, they theorize, is a dysfunction in the person's neurophysiologic feedback loops (remember social learning theory's *discriminatory functions*). They suggest the alcoholic simply lacks the ability to identify his level of intoxication. Impairment in speech and other motor activities that provide the cue to non-alcoholics to reduce intake do not function normally in the alcoholic drinker.

A UNIFIED APPROACH

The stage was set for an evolution of the models developed by the various schools of thought prominent in psychology during the last few decades. The rapid influx of various disciplines into the field of addiction treatment created a plethora of tools for the therapist to draw upon. It also created, however, a quagmire of confusing and sometimes contradictory descriptions of the etiology of the condition as well as the recommended interventions.

I am strongly in agreement with Miller and Hester (1989) who warn us against becoming "undisciplined eclectics" in our desire to avoid being trapped by one single mode of treatment. These authors also argue against three myths about alcoholism treatment: 1) Nothing works, 2) There is one particular approach which is superior to all others, and 3) All treatment approaches work about equally well (p.3). They suggest, rather, that the research shows that some treatment is better than none at all, that various approaches have appeal and effectiveness to various individuals, and that the best treatment is the one best matched to the client's particular problems and needs. This forms the basis for their proposed *informed eclecticism* where the therapist first assesses the needs of the client, then tailors the interventions to the individual utilizing the most appropriate techniques for the specific problems identified.

Donovan and Chaney (1985) also propose an emergent multivarient approach to alcoholism which allows *constructive alternativism* to overcome controversy between conflicting models. This is accomplished by incorporating factors from each model that encourage an emergent position. Such a position emphasizes a multivariate approach to addiction and alcoholism "...which implies multiple causality, multiple system involvement, and multiple levels of analyses" (p. 355).

Donovan (1988) presents a powerful argument for an *emergent model of addictive behaviors*. Based on commonalities across addictive behaviors, he espouses a *biopsychosocial* model of addiction and treatment. This model draws upon all the approaches listed above and others as a composite that addresses the genesis and progression of addictive disorders and presents a flexible method of treatment.

FINAL WORDS

It would seem that the therapist's own theory of the etiology of the disease will influence his expectations for the outcome of treatment.[7] If the literature is to be believed, then we need to focus our attentions on *current behaviors* if we are to help those who seek our guidance. To effectively alter the course of the addiction, the counselor or therapist and client need to meet with an understanding that certain behaviors (thoughts, actions, emotions, etc.) will need to be explored and agree that some of them will need to be changed. Effective treatment inevitably results in what addictions counselors commonly call *life style change*. Life style change occurs when there is a pervasive alteration in the addict's thoughts, beliefs and responses to the world around him or her.

NOTES FOR CHAPTER 2

1. According to Jacobson (1989), Jellinek (1960) included in this review, "...notions of sin and faulty religious training; nutritional deficiencies; allergies; abnormal biochemistry; brain pathology; neurosis; endocrinologic disorders; heredity and genetics; and social and cultural background" (p. 18).

2. For an excellent summary of this dilemma and the changes in the field of addictions research and treatment, see Miller & Hester (1989) and Donovan (1988), who presents a viable alternative to the confusion found in the field.

3. This quote comes from the letter by Dr. Silkworth that appears at the beginning of *Alcoholics Anonymous* (Alcoholics Anonymous World Services, 1976, p. xxvi). The letter itself is introduced with the statement that "...he confirms what we who have suffered alcoholic torture must believe – that the body of the alcoholic is quite as abnormal as his mind" (p. xxiv).

4. I am a strong advocate for group processes in working with addictive disorders. Most of the techniques presented in this book are readily utilized in group formats. Group work has the added advantage of assisting a number of clients simultaneously.

5. See Bandura (1977) for the basics of the social learning theory model. Applications of this model to addictions can be found in Nathan (1980).

6. There is a strong indication here that treatment will extend beyond the expected very brief therapy usually encountered by patients of NLP. This is supported by research on the ability of the recovering addict/alcoholic to learn, practice, and assimilate new behaviors and skills as well documented by Miller (1989). This model also strongly supports the need for the recovering client to include other means for supporting and reinforcing their therapeutic changes, such as ongoing participation in a Twelve Step program (see Chapter 4).

7. In fact, Ellis, McInerney, DiGiuseppe, and Yeager (1988) quite eloquently state, "...theories of etiology can be taken as excuses not to intervene because the hypothesized etiological factors are so 'deep,' pervasive, or biological..." that intervention is useless (p. 22).

ASSESSMENT AND MOTIVATION

Almost everything that

the American public believes to be

the scientific truth about alcoholism is false

(Fingarette, 1988, p. 1).

O f the various stages of treatment, I believe assessment is the most important. The assessment provides the basis for our interventions. Properly utilized, it can shape the entire therapeutic episode. One ingredient that appears to be common to good assessment strategies is the evaluation of the client's motivation to engage in the therapeutic processes. What sequence of events cause a person to become motivated? Especially with addiction, what role does motivation play in the recovery processes? These are some of the questions we will visit in this chapter.

During my years working in the field, however, I have found that both motivation and assessment are often misunderstood. A major cause of these misunderstandings are the many popular misperceptions and beliefs regarding addiction. As discussed in the previous chapter, these beliefs influence our own attitudes towards our clients and their problems. The more alert we are to our biases, the more we can prevent the "fish in the dreams" problems that arise from judgments and pro-mote inadequate assessments.

This chapter will focus on these issues and prepare a foundation for the techniques that follow in the remaining sections of this book.

DEFINING ADDICTION

Before we can assess addiction, we must first define it. This will require some differentiation between the terms *addiction* and *dependence*. Historically, one of the problems in defining addiction is that there is considerable misunderstanding of the relationship between *physical dependence* and addiction.[1] The architects of the early models of addiction used what are commonly called "hard drugs" — opiates like morphine and heroin — as the basis for construction of their models. This resulted in the models including both *tolerance* and *physical dependence* in their definitions.

We define addiction as compulsion to use a drug, loss of control over the amount used, and continued use in spite of adverse consequences (Smith and Wesson, 1988, p. 11).

In these models, the assumption is that a person must exhibit physical withdrawal symptoms in order to be diagnosed as drug or alcohol dependent or *addicted*.

There has been a trend with more recent theories of addiction to broaden this definition significantly. In most of the current definitions, physical withdrawals are not prerequisite to a diagnosis of dependence or addiction. This in turn, has broadened the scope of behaviors considered to be addictive, including such disorders as gambling and over-eating. One major result of this expanded definition of addiction is that it opens the door to application of treatment methodologies to a much broader range of problem behaviors. It is exciting and rewarding to watch this expanding field of addictions counseling regularly addressing new varieties of problems.

Fingarette (1988) is one of many authors who has grappled with the problem of diverse and inconsistent definitions of addiction. Drawing from the work of other researchers[2], he notes that there are three major views of the etiology of alcoholism. These include medical, psychological, and sociocultural views. He suggests that nearly every conceivable perspective has been adopted in trying to explain the causes of alcoholism but none of them has achieved general scientific acceptance. Fingarette agrees with the proposal that perhaps a little of each view is true. If so, he points out, we are left with alcoholism as a disease that is "multiple in origin and complex in development." He goes on to suggest that, "Instead of a single disease and syndrome (cluster of symptoms), we have a continuum of behaviors ranging from teetotaling to chronic heavy abuse" (p. 50).

In one of many volumes on the subject, I found another description that represents fairly well my own thinking on the subject. In his very thorough treatise on assessment of alcoholism, Jacobson (1989) introduces the concept of *multiple alcoholisms* which he found useful to guide research, diagnosis, and treatment of the disorder. Jacobson supports his notion of multiple alcoholisms with the fact that there are so many different models of alcoholism and that each is thoroughly researched and viable, "...with its own ultimately identifiable etiology, course and development, treatment, prognosis, and outcome" (p. 18). Because of the efficacy of these very different models, he argues for a *multivariate view* of alcoholism. This is yet another example of the emergent paradigm discussed in the last chapter.

Another researcher in the field (Donovan, 1988) writes that addiction is "...a complex, progressive behavior pattern having biological, psychological, sociological, and behavioral components" (pp. 5–6). Donovan also echoes the trend toward more flexible definitions that encompass a variety of aspects of the client's experience.

Borrowing from the field of medicine, many writers are now using the term *biopsychosocial disease*.[3] With this term we encompass all the primary elements of the disorder in one word, giving us perhaps the most concise definition arising from this trend. This definition addresses the *biological* aspects of the disorder, such as the degradation of the various organs of the body, the habituation to the substance usually result-ing in physical withdrawal symptoms and other aspects of the body's response to the repeated expo-sure to the drug or compulsive activity. It also includes the *psychological* results of addiction, including the stress-reducing qualities of certain activities, emotional dependence, and other coping behaviors. Finally, this definition includes the *social* problems encountered by the inevitable deterioration of the person's inner and outer worlds.

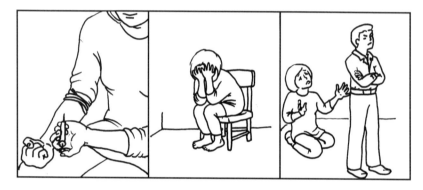

BIO PSYCHO SOCIAL DISEASE

USE, ABUSE, OR DEPENDENCE

Another area of confusion encountered in the field of addictions is the difference between *use, abuse,* and *dependence.* What constitutes normal social use as opposed to abuse of mood-altering substances? It was easy when I was working for the U.S. Army. By their own definition, use of any illegal drug was considered drug abuse. Jaffe (1980) proposes a definition of drug abuse using a form of *social diagnosis*: drug abuse is the "...use, usually by self administration, of any drug in a manner that deviates from the approved medical or social patterns within a given culture" (p. 535). If we view the Army as its own subculture, having its own standards and code of conduct, this definition works quite well.

Using social diagnosis as the defining parameters for drug abuse, however, does not adequately address other points of view. It does not, for example differentiate between experimental, recreational, or occasional use patterns found with many illegal drug users. Of course, these patterns are also found at the early stages of the addictive process. What we need, to paraphrase Smith and Wesson (1988, p. 10), is a way to diagnosis addictive disorders that can make a distinction between *noncompulsive sociorecreational* use and abuse that requires treatment.

DEFINITIONS FROM THE FIELD

The World Health Organization (WHO) has a long-standing definition that has a general appeal. It springs from the old-school concept that addiction was indicated by the presence of withdrawal distress when the drug use ended. The WHO definition essentially is: psychological dependence plus tolerance plus physical dependence equals addiction. While this definition is adequate for most substances in the later stages of addiction, it does not cover the incidence of compulsive use of certain obsessive drugs such as cocaine *even in the absence of withdrawal symptoms*, nor does it adequately address other compulsive disorders.

In addition to the example of drug abuse I gave at the beginning of this section, while in Germany working with the ADAPCP, we had an operational definition of addiction that appeared to fit most situations. Addiction was defined as compulsive use, characterized by an overwhelming involvement with the use of a drug, the securing of its supply, and a high tendency to relapse. However, this definition also falls just a bit short of a generally inclusive description.

The physician's "bible" of diagnostic categories, *DSM-IV* (APA, 1994), labels addiction to chemicals as substance dependence. Requiring the patient to demonstrate or report at least three of seven symptoms for the diagnosis, this format has a great deal of flexibility and facilitates a diagnosis that addresses the concerns expressed by Smith and Wesson above. In simple terms, the seven areas are (p. 181):

- evidence of tolerance

- evidence of withdrawal

- using more or longer than planned

- having a persistent desire or unsuccessful attempts to reduce or control use

- spending a great deal of time obtaining, using, or recovering from the effects of the substance

- reducing or not attending important social, occupational, or recreational activities because of substance use

- continuing to use after identifying that social, psychological, or physical problems are being caused or exacerbated by the substance

The manual indicates that in order to be considered, the symptoms must have been present "...at any time in the same 12-month period" (p. 181). The diagnosis can also include what are called *course specifiers* which indicate partial, early, sustained, or full remission of the disorder and also whether the individual is in a controlled environment or on special medication to control drug use such as disulferum (antabuse) or naltrexon.

Substance abuse is differentiated from the above diagnosis in several ways. It is described as a "...maladaptive pattern of substance use..." which requires only one or more of the following four symptoms (pps. 182-183):

- using has resulted in absences, poor performance or other problems with major role obligations

- repeated use in dangerous situations

- repeated drug-related legal problems

- continuing to use after identifying that social, psychological, or physical problems are being caused or exacerbated by the substance

For all its flexibility and breadth of scope, however, there is one problem with this system of diagnosis: it includes vague and subjective terms. Father Martin (1989), in his entertaining and instructive book, *Chalk Talk*, clearly underscores a major problem of diagnosis when he stated, "I would like to bet that any one of you who is experiencing trouble with your own drinking will give a descriptive definition that will not include yourself. For example, if you are a weekend drinker, isn't it obvious that an alcoholic is someone who drinks every day? If you get drunk occasionally, isn't it obvious that an alcoholic is somebody who gets drunk every time he drinks?" (p. 34).

The description Father Martin presented above is what Rogers and McMillin (1989) call "comparing out". It works like this: when examining their drinking behaviors to see if they exhibit any of the signs of "alcoholism," problem drinkers will discover there are *some* symptoms they *don't* have. Thus, they conclude, they can't possibly be alcoholic. Of course, this whole process is

COMPARING OUT

based on the faulty premise that one must have *all* the symptoms to have the disease.

Returning to the symptoms as defined by *DSM-IV*, how do we determine such objective variables as "persistent", or "a great deal of time", or "important"? If, as Father Martin pointed out, we ourselves are abusing the substance, it is likely that our natural inclination will be to define these concepts in relation to our own behaviors. In such a case, then, the seven descriptions might be considered as symptoms only if they happen more than they happen to me! And we don't have to be abusing to be inconsistent in our application of these guidelines. Our own personal beliefs about addiction will influence how we assess the client's behaviors against such vague descriptions.

Let us close this discussion with one final entry. Drawing again from Smith and Wesson (1988) but broadening their original concept somewhat, I would like to propose the following definition of addiction: *A compulsion to use a drug or initiate an activity, loss of control over the amount used or the time or duration of use/activity, and continued use/activity despite adverse consequences.* Although not as concrete as the *DSM-IV* criteria, this description seems to fit the broadest spectrum of disorders while being sensitive to those excluded by some of the others. It is the definition we will employ for the remainder of this book.

THE LOSS OF CONTROL ISSUE

Loss of control is another concept that is either misunderstood or not completely understood. As a counselor in the field, I frequently need to explain that loss of control does not mean doing crazy things while under the influence. A normally calm and shy individual who gets into fights when intoxicated or someone who runs around ripping antennas off of cars in a parking lot is not

...if an alcoholic takes a drink, he can never be sure he will be able to stop (Mark Keller, 1972, p. 160).

experiencing the type of loss of control we confront in treating addictive disorders. This individual is exhibiting *antisocial behavior* which is a problem or symptom in its own right. Loss of control with regards to drug and alcohol use and other compulsive disorders refers to the using act itself.

The most commonly held belief about loss of control has to do with what happens when a person starts using or engaging in the compulsive activity. Briefly stated, this is the belief that once started, the alcoholic or addict can't stop. This has given rise to such sayings as "one is too many and twenty is not enough!" Although there is controversy surrounding this concept — many cognitive behaviorists believe that early stage alcohol abuse is amenable to CBT — there is also evidence that later stages of addiction have more deep-rooted basis for the problem. Blum and Payne (1991) note that when alcoholics put alcohol or other mood-altering drugs into their systems, it causes alterations in brain chemistry that result in a "biopsychosocial craving dynamic". The addict becomes uncertain whether or not he or she will be able to stop. This is one definition of loss of control. In the early stages of the disease, this problem is only intermittent. Eventually, however, it progresses to loss of control at almost every use.

There is another aspect of this problem that occurs *between* use episodes. There are actually two distinct aspects of loss of control. The first we have already discussed where the addict experiences the inability to control *how much* (or *how long* with compulsive activities) he or she will use once started. The second, however, is just as important. This is where the person experiences loss of control over *when* he or she is going to use or engage in the compulsive activity. The key to understanding loss of control is the idea of *predictability*: the addict cannot accurately predict either when or how much of the drug he or she will use. It is this inability to predict use that demarcates addictive use from experimental or social use. This aspect of addiction also forms the First Step in the Twelve Step Programs (see Chapter 4), in which the individual admits that he or she is "powerless" over the drug or compulsion.

THE ROLE OF DENIAL

For those working with addiction, it is critical to have a thorough understanding of denial. This much maligned coping strategy, poorly understood by many, can be conceived of as the "capstone" of the addictive process. As the addiction progresses, addicts build internal walls to protect and insulate themselves from the consequences of their abuse. Denial fulfills the crucial role of holding this whole distorted system together. In fact, Jellinek (1960) identified denial as a "hallmark characteristic" of the alcoholic.

Denial is what helps people from feeling pain or looking at a difficult situation. Denial helps illness and problems continue to grow (Dene Stamas, 1981, p. 77).

It is not surprising, then, that Blum and Payne (1991) call denial "the first obstacle on the alcoholic's road to recovery" (p. 41). Whether a person turns to alcohol, mood-altering drugs, or other compulsive activities, the initial motivation to use is reinforced by pleasure, by a sense of relief, or by a combination of both. Of course, these are the reasons that any person uses or engages in such activities. Over time, however, some individuals come to *depend* on the drug to supply the relief, the pleasure, or to cope with life in other ways.

As addiction progresses the individual begins to shy away from recognizing the problems because the activity is meeting such important needs. Anything that might threaten his or her only means of obtaining the pleasure, relief or the ability to cope is rejected by the addict. Even when confronted with the inevitable loss of control, the individual is unwilling to admit that the drug is stronger than his or her willpower. Finally, in the later stages, the addict/alcoholic feels compelled to deny the addiction, because it has become the only source of relief from the pain of the disease itself.

In my first book (Lewis and Pucelik, 1982), we discussed how people build models or maps of experience that guide them through life. We utilize basic building blocks called *representational systems* to create these guiding and coping strategies. Rather than being accurate representations of reality, however, our maps and models are inevitably flawed. This is because during the process of constructing these models, we utilize three *universal human modeling processes*. These are the processes of *generalization*, *deletion*, and *distortion*. Based on specific strands of experiences called *4-tuples* (each moment in time includes each of the representations of experience: visual, kinesthetic, auditory, and olfactory/gustatory), our internal maps allow us to function efficiently in an environment that bombards us with millions of bits of stimuli every second.

What happens, however, when these 4-tuples of experience become distorted by the effects of drugs or compulsive behaviors such as gambling or eat-purge activities? Built into these strands of experience will be sensations that are strongly affected by the drug, the "high" of the gambler's rush, or the "craving-to-bursting" of the binge eater. They will also include the perceptual distortions resulting from the effects of the drug on the person's senses (seeing, feeling, hearing, taste/smell). Many of these 4-tuples of experience will be incorporated into the models and maps that guide the person's behavior, thoughts, dreams, emotions, and shape his or her perceptions of reality[4].

Melody Beattie (1986), in one of the short Hazelden booklets describes denial: "You may feel uneasy, anxious, afraid, or downright desperate. Something isn't right, but you can't figure it out. You may have a vague idea what the problem involves; you may say it aloud sometimes. Others may be pointing it out to you in specific terms. But you don't hear yourself or them. You can't believe it!" (p. 1). Gorski (1989) underscores this by stating, "Most chemically dependent people don't think about their drinking and drug use. We have trained ourselves to avoid thinking about it. This is what denial is all about" (p. 82). Beebe (1990) takes a more clinical stance. He describes denial as unconscious processes that include suppression, repression, projection, and rationalization. These are strategies our clients use to promote a belief that addiction is not a problem and that their lives are "normal". One of the most obvious ways that denial works was previously discussed. The process of *comparing out* is a form of rationalization where the drinker systematically rules out alcoholism as applied to him based on the fact that he doesn't have *all* the symptoms.

One creative description of denial that I particularly like comes from Stamas (1981). He notes that denial is a process that prevents us from feeling pain or from taking care of difficult situations. He uses the analogy of a visit to the dentist. Denial is like a shot of Novocain, in that it takes away the pain without fixing the problem. In fact, regular doses of denial (Novocain) only encourage the problem (cavity) to worsen because it can be easily ignored. Eventually, however, the condition becomes life-threatening.

DENIAL

Gorski and Miller (1986) describe how denial develops simultaneously with the other problems associated with addiction. They point out that addiction is a chronic disease, meaning it takes time to fully develop. Because becoming addicted is a gradual process, the addict and his or her family simply adapt to the problems and adjust their lives around the compulsion. However, this compensating occurs at an unconscious level and promotes unhealthy patterns of coping that foster denial. Denial of the disease then becomes an integral part of the disease itself. These authors chronicle three stages in the development of denial: "The addicted person is able to deny the existence of the addiction because in the early stage there are no physical or behavioral problems; in the middle stage problems are not associated with using; and in the chronic stage thinking is impaired and judgment is distorted" (p. 48).

Denial is a concept that is sometimes grossly misrepresented. I had a friend who attended a conference on Adult Children of Alcoholics and other dysfunctional families. The leader of the conference stood in front of the gathering of over 500 participants and asked everyone who had come from a dysfunctional family to raise their hands. After a moment, she then stated: "Look around you. Anyone who does not have his or her hand up is in denial!" The implication, of course, is that not admitting a dysfunction is a symptom of denial. While it is true that this is an important piece of this process, to assume that *anyone* who will not admit to dysfunction is *ipso facto* in denial has led to some confusion about this subject.[5]

ABSTINENCE VS. MODERATION

In assessing addiction, it is critical for the counselor to determine how far it has progressed. Determining the degree of dysfunction is important for a number of reasons. The outcome of the assessment will influence the formation of an effective treatment plan. I like the analogy that Vaillant (1983) uses in which he likens the disease of alcoholism to the disease of essential hypertension. Both diseases develop along a continuum. If detected in the early stages, treatment of hypertension involves helping the patient change his or her life-style including diet, physical activity, and habits of coping with stress and other life situations. The same approaches are involved in treating early stages of addiction where strict medical interventions are not required.

As both these diseases progress, however, the emphasis begins to shift. More attention needs to be paid to medical issues such as dietary deficiencies, organ malfunction, etc. In fact, at the late stage of either disease, intense medical intervention may be required just to keep the patient alive. Especially during the initial phases of treatment, life-style counseling will take a secondary position to more immediate stabilizing medical interventions.

Another reason to assess the progression of the disease is the need to identify and address what is often called the *controlled drinking* issue. This is the idea that a problem drinker or drug user might eventually return to social use[6]. Many of our clients come into treatment following a *motivating crisis*, an often abrupt and sometimes severe consequence of their abuse. They are looking for help in resolving their current problems so that they can return to "normal living." We need to understand that, for many of these clients, normal *includes* their drinking, or drugging, gambling, etc. If we overlook this belief at the onset, we may set them up for failure in the future. Here also is one of those areas where the *counselor's* beliefs will strongly influence the therapeutic outcome. Let's look more closely at this issue.

It is not unusual for people entering treatment for addiction or compulsive disorders, especially the first time, to want to return to use. Because denial influences addicts' perceptions of their condition, this goal may often be unconscious or unspoken. The problem is there are several diametrically opposed points of view in treatment that address this often "hidden" agenda. These views, arising from one or another of the many diverse models of addiction covered in the last chapter, encourage radically disparate approaches to treatment.

One of the cornerstones of many treatment programs is the edict: "Once addicted, you can never return to social use." Period. Depending on your theoretical bias, you may agree that this should always be stated up front or not. In the AA or medical models, for example, abstinence is the rule. However, there are alternative points of view, especially from the CBT perspective. Ellis, et. al. (1988) specifically points out that a significant controversy exists between CBT and the medical model when addressing the issue of controlled drinking. He notes that, "...a client's choice of treatment goals may hinge upon the *therapist's* views regarding this issue" (italics mine, p. 15). My goal here is not to argue which point of view is correct, but rather to open the door during the assessment phase of treatment to the idea that one approach may be more appropriate for the particular client sitting before us than another.

There is substantial research that demonstrates that not all problem drinkers become alcohol dependent (Fingarette, 1988, Ellis, et. al. , 1988). According to some reports, a significant percentage of alcoholics (19% according to Miller and Hester, 1980) exhibit a return of "control" by either quitting or returning to asymptomatic drinking. If you believe the validity of these reports, then your treatment approaches may be dramatically different from a counselor who absolutely adheres to the American Disease Model. As Ellis pointed out, the counselor's beliefs are a major factor in the options presented to the client as possible therapeutic outcomes.

From a purely cognitive behavioral point of view, compulsive use is an indication of poorly constructed strategies or irrational thoughts. Maultsby (1978), for example, asserts that problem drinkers develop their addiction as a result of habitually drinking (or using other drugs) to obtain relief from their emotions. They eventually become "mentally dependent" on the alcohol to feel better. While he does not deny the existence of physical dependence, it is downplayed in his approach to treatment. In Maultsby's approach, alcohol and drug abuse are learned behaviors, and thus are amenable to alteration through s that work with a person's beliefs and coping strategies. When a person learns to deal with life, emotions, stress, etc. without resorting to alcohol or drug use, that person could arguably return to normal social use.

I want to underscore here, however, that evidence of the success of controlled drinking approaches remains controversial. I recommend any therapist utilizing such a regimen familiarize him or herself with the literature on the subject.[7] It may also be wise to follow the experience of others in the field of CBT who recommend *against* a goal of controlled drinking in certain cases. Ellis, for example (Ellis, et. al. 1988), warns that controlled drinking techniques would only be appropriate if the client is not "highly physically dependent" on alcohol and does not have a long history of alcohol-related problems. He also suggests that these clients would also need to be evaluated for willingness to work very hard at reasserting control over their use. As stated earlier, then, a thorough assessment of the degree of dysfunction and the duration of the problem are critical in assigning appropriate treatment goals. In addition, we need to screen for motivation to work towards the therapeutic goals. Motivation will be covered in detail shortly.

After reviewing the literature on the abstinence *vs.* moderation issue, Vuchinich, Tucker, and Harllee (1988) outlined several "rules of thumb" the therapist can use as contraindications for a goal of "reduced consumption" for alcoholics. An abbreviated version of their list includes the presence of any of the following:

- Liver disease.
- Psychiatric disorders or use of medications that would be adversely affected by alcohol.
- A history of pathological use associated with violence or bizarre behaviors.
- Indications of physiological dependence (tolerance and withdrawals).
- The client's own request for abstinence as a goal.
- Lack of environmental support for moderation (p. 70).

If you prefer, however, easy guidelines were established by Donovan and Chaney (1985). Citing a number of researchers, they suggest controlled drinking should be ruled out for any individuals "who evidence a recent physiological addiction to alcohol" (p. 363).

POLYDRUG ABUSE AND OTHER COMPULSIONS

When discussing the abuse of one or another drug, there are many variables to consider. For example, if an individual is addicted to a prescription drug, following treatment, is a return to use medically indicated? Another example is the controversy in some circles regarding marijuana: is it or is it not *addictive*[8]?

There are also certain drugs that warrant special attention because of their potency. Cocaine and heroin both fall into a category sometimes called *obsessive* drugs. These are drugs that can trigger obsessive thoughts with as little as one or two doses. Abuse of drugs from this group often results in rapid onset of psychological dependence leading to physical dependence. The processes involved in obtaining and using such drugs generally place an individual at high risk of serious illness and legal complications. In addition, the ability of users to maintain moderate levels of use of these drugs over time appears to be extremely low.

If our client presents with a history of abuse of several mood-altering substances (including alcohol) at one time, we will often find the problems have compounded greatly. This is known as *polydrug abuse*: when no one drug dominates the abuse pattern. There are additional complications when dealing with polydrug abuse or addiction, especially during early stages of treatment and detoxification. However, the general direction of treatment and recovery following stabilization will generally follow a similar path, regardless of the drug or drugs abused.

This book seeks to address other compulsive behaviors in addition to drug and alcohol abuse. These include, for example, gambling and eating disorders. We can ask similar questions about the treatment and recovery of these behavioral addictions as well. Following treatment, can a compulsive gambler return to normal non-compulsive gambling? A client with an eating disorder must continue to eat; therefore, moderation is not a choice but rather a requirement. What happens when we find chemical and non-chemical compulsions combined in one person? We sometimes find, for example, certain sexual compulsions associated with cocaine addiction. Should both disorders be treated at the same time, or should they be dealt with separately[9]?

It is during the assessment phase of treatment that we begin to build a model of the client's problems. The biological areas are the most important to address initially. The realm of medical interventions are beyond the scope of this book. However, once stabilized, we can begin to work with the client's thought processes, beliefs, strategies, and personal relationships. Our assessment will provide the hierarchy of needs that we use to build a treatment plan for each client. It is during this process we need to ask the questions posed above.

As with any disorder, response to treatment varies greatly from one client to the next. Some of the factors involved in treatment success include the duration and the degree of dysfunction, environment, and motivation. As important as the other areas in the client's presentation, assessing the patient's motivation is critical to the formation of the treatment plan. It is to this factor we now turn our attention.

MOTIVATION

During his introduction to a seminar on "Health and Belief Systems" a few years ago, Robert Dilts spoke at length about recovering cancer patients. At one point he stated, "If somebody is ready to change, all you have to do is [blow] and they change." He pointed out that at that point, it doesn't even matter what type of therapeutic technique is utilized, because change is *inevitable*.[10] After working in the field of addictions for a number of years, I know that this is true. While I have treated many very difficult cases, I have had numerous clients who walked into my office and virtually metamorphosed in front of my eyes. Why? What kind of magic caused such rapid therapeutic change? Most importantly, how do we get our patients or our friends or loved ones who are caught in their addiction to that point? Is there something we can do to set up this kind of change?

...motivation can be understood not as something one has but rather as something one does. It involves recognizing a problem, searching for a way to change, and, then beginning, continuing, and, complying with that change strategy, (William R. Miller, 1989, p. 69).

The answer to the last question is "yes". The key to any change is motivation. Although there has been quite a bit of study of this complex internal process, it has only been recently that there were any clear models that can help us understand it. The following outlines some of the research on motivation and includes one very pragmatic theory we might use to help our clients "get to that point."

WHAT MOTIVATION IS NOT

Before we define motivation, let's take a quick look at what it *isn't!* Motivation is often erroneously viewed as some sort of "personality trait", something people "have" that enables them to achieve their goals. When addicts or alcoholics fail in early recovery, many shrug their shoulders and write them off with the idea that they just didn't "have enough motivation" to quit. Such a belief can have devastating consequences if held by either the addict's counselor or the addict himself, causing poor self-esteem and unproductive shame and guilt. Gorski and Miller (1982, 1986) propose that this mistaken belief may eventually cause addicts to question their sanity, especially those who *want* to stop, but find themselves repeatedly cycling through a relapse pattern.

The tragedy of such irrational thinking can be heard daily at Twelve Step meetings and in treatment programs. As they share their experiences, alcoholics, addicts, gamblers and sufferers of other compulsive addictions regularly expose the myth of *lack* of motivation. Through heart-wrenching stories of pain

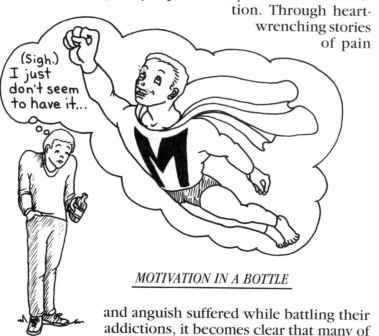

(Sigh.) I just don't seem to have it...

MOTIVATION IN A BOTTLE

and anguish suffered while battling their addictions, it becomes clear that many of these individuals have been *tremendously* motivated to quit, but simply lacked the tools to do so. The question often asked a new member of a Twelve Step Program is, "Are you willing to go to any lengths to quit?" Although the answer is often "yes," the task is confounding to many. And the problem is exacerbated by professional people helpers who are unable to adequately address the sense of helplessness and hopelessness that plagues many chronic relapsers. To blame the client for not trying hard enough, for lacking the motivation or for being "resistant" is the worst thing we can do.

While we are on the subject of unhelpful counselor beliefs, another "professional excuse" for counselors' failure with alcoholic/addict clients is to blame it on their denial. We have already discussed how denial prevents a person from feeling pain, anxiety, anger, frustration, guilt, remorse, etc. caused by his or her habit. This results in the addict continuing to seek relief from physical withdrawals or from inadequate coping strategies through abuse of the drugs or destructive compulsions. The use of the drugs or compulsive behaviors themselves mask the feelings the addict is attempting to escape, while providing temporary relief from the other more obvious symptoms of addiction. But it is not simply their *denial* that perpetuates the problem once they have entered treatment, but rather a combination of dysfunctional beliefs, poor coping strategies, a non-supportive environment, etc. Assessment is an ongoing process throughout the therapeutic relationship. When we encounter problems with treatment adherence, lack of progress or "denial" and "resistance", it is time to reassess the treatment plan and begin to explore alternative interventions.

To reiterate, when encountering a client who chronically relapses, the therapist could use any of the following excuses: "His denial is too strong," "She hasn't hit bottom yet," or "He isn't motivated enough to quit." However, none of these excuses addresses the problem, because they place blame on some intangible quality within the client. What we need to do in such cases is reassess our interventions and identify where we need to change the therapeutic process! Please don't misunderstand: I am not implying that we will be successful with every client every time! Addiction can outfox even the most skilled counselor. To paraphrase *Alcoholics Anonymous* (1976), remember that we are dealing with addiction – cunning, baffling, and powerful (pp. 58-59). My point is that we need to be alert to personal beliefs which may impede our flexibility in working with these clients.

You may remember from the introduction, one of my all-time favorite slogans learned during my early training with Richard Bandler and John Grinder applies here: *If what you're doing isn't working, try something else!*

WHAT IS MOTIVATION?

We know that there are external factors that impact the progression of the disease of addiction. Denial, for example, though often believed to be an attribute of a person, is actually the result of complex interactions between the addict, his peers, family, subculture, co-workers, employers, teachers, etc. During the developing addiction, these interactions conspire to help the addict ignore the pain and avoid the consequences of the compulsive behavior. However, it is also these same people who are often the most effective means for motivating the individual to seek treatment and make changes toward a more healthy lifestyle.

One effective method, known as a *classic intervention*, specifically utilizes the people in the addict's life to create a "motivating life crisis" that will result in the alcoholic/addict voluntarily entering treatment. Through the pioneering work of Vernon Johnson (1980), the Johnson Institute has researched and developed this particular strategy for helping the families of the alcoholic/addict by providing counseling, coaching, and support during a choreographed confrontation with the addict. The goal of the confrontation is to move the addict from passive inactivity into treatment.

In reviewing some of the research on motivation, I ran across an interesting sidebar. One researcher (Miller, 1989) points to evidence of a "therapist effect" on the outcome of treatment for alcoholism. In his review of outcomes, Miller points out that counselors with more "motivated" patients tend to have certain characteristics and styles. He states that the more successful clients work with therapists who are more empathetic, optimistic, and take an active interest in the client's welfare. This echoes a point made in my last book (Lewis and Pucelik, 1982) that the ability to gain rapport with clients is an attribute of successful therapists and counselors.

STAGE MODEL OF MOTIVATION

Let us set aside the external factors associated with motivation now and take a look at the client himself. There appears to be a sequence of events an individual will normally experience as part of the process of making changes. Change doesn't happen at a whim. Generally, we attempt to maintain homeostasis (status quo) during ordinary activities. However, we will change our behavior in response to certain internal or external cues, such as hunger, pain, or perceived threat that cause within us an action-oriented *arousal state*. It is this state of arousal that we usually identify as motivation.

Prochaska and DiClemente (1982) have developed a simple but very useful model of the change process which includes six succinctly defined steps or stages. One pragmatic aspect of this model is that each stage clearly indicates how one type of therapeutic intervention will be more effective at that particular stage than another. Once you have assessed what stage the client is at in the change process, you can design an appropriate intervention that will capitalize on this natural sequence of motivating events.

The first step in the model is *precontemplation*. Prior to any awareness of a problem, the client operates freely in the naiveté of his world of drug/alcohol abuse or compulsivity. The lack of conscious awareness may be the result of denial mechanisms, or simply that there have been too few significant problems to bring the compulsion to the attention of the individual. The most effective interventions at this stage include strong educational components designed to help clients identify consequences of their compulsive behaviors. Of course, at this point in the addictive cycle, it may require a great deal of education and confrontation just to convince a client that there even is a problem, much less that he or she needs to make changes.

One area where this stage of change is important to consider is in *prevention* where we are counseling clients (or students or our children) about the risks of *beginning* to use. Since there are no negative consequences for the client/student/child to draw from personally, we must tactfully build a presentation that they can relate to *as if* they had. This may soon become even more important, as research over the last few decades supports evidence of a genetic predisposition for alcoholism (Blum and Payne, 1991). We appear to be close to identifying a specific genetic marker for this "inherited" tendency toward alcoholism. Once such a marker has been identified, it can be used in counseling individuals about the potential risks they may face *before* they start drinking. Of course, as noted in Chapter 1, not having this genetic predisposition does not preclude possible addiction to alcohol, and the jury is still out on other drugs and compulsive disorders.

The next stage is *contemplation*. In this stage the client has become aware that something is amiss but feels ambivalent about the problem. This person is not likely to put forth much effort into change without an increase in one or more internal or external cues to cause an arousal state. Prochaska and DiClemente liken this stage to a seesaw or teeter-totter. On one end is the addicted part, and on the other is the part that recognizes the problem and wants to change. The ambivalence encountered here is the result of various dissociated "parts" of the individual[11].

Gorski (1989) talks about *internal dissonance* that occurs between a person's addictive-self and his sober-self when he or she starts thinking about using. On the positive side, we can see this dissonance as an indication that a person is no longer comfortable with his or her addiction. However, the strength of the addicted-self, combined with the client's vulnerability to the pleasure (and absence of pain) of the euphoric state, make therapeutic changes particularly susceptible to sabotage by unintegrated aspects of the personality. At this stage, again, strong educational interventions can prove helpful in changing the "balance" of power in the system.

INTERNAL DISSONANCE

I should point out here the important role which attendance at Twelve Step meetings can play in the educational process. For many years, it was believed that recovery from alcoholism could not begin until the alcoholic had "hit bottom". This meant the addict had to become "personally bankrupt" through the loss of all that was important to him, including his job, family, and health. As stated in the *Twelve Steps and Twelve Traditions* (AA, 1953), "...only through utter defeat are we able to take our first steps toward liberation and strength" (p. 21).[12]

However, as the program of AA continued to grow, it was discovered that by sharing their personal stories with other problem drinkers, it was possible to "...raise the bottom the rest of us had hit to the point where it would hit them" (p. 23). By attending Twelve Step speakers meetings, our clients can vicariously experience the results of the progression of their disease through the stories of others in recovery.[13] This kind of educational experience is sometimes enough to "tip the scales" on the teeter totter in favor of recovery and away from the patterns of continued denial.

Following contemplation, a person enters a brief stage called *determination*. At this third step in the process the client decides it is time to change. This is the almost magical moment Dilts talked about in which all the therapist has to do is blow lightly, and the client virtually "falls" into the change. This is a very critical point at which the "window" to change opens. What makes it so critical is the brevity of this temporary opening.

Therapists working regularly with addiction will recognize that this is the phase of change that often needs to be the *initial goal state* for the counseling. Arriving at this point often requires a great deal of finesse and patience on the part of the therapist. Once there, however, the tone of the counseling changes dramatically. At this stage, the therapist can most effectively intervene by supporting the client's tenuous decision to start to make changes, continuing to provide feedback and information that reinforce the shift of balance.

MOTIVATIONAL CRISES

The determination stage is often precipitated by a *motivational crisis*, some catastrophe or tragic event in the client's life that swings the balance of the status quo teeter-totter abruptly in favor of change. Gorski and Miller (1982) define this crisis as "...an event that results in the alcoholic recognizing that something is seriously wrong, that there has been a pattern of progressive problems, and that he needs help in understanding and solving those problems" (p. 49). We must remember, however, that even in the face of extreme situations such as loss of job, threat of divorce, incarceration, serious medical complications, etc., well-established patterns of denial continue to operate. These patterns can easily bring a return of the client's previous ambivalence.[14] This is one reason why it is important to assess and identify this open window period.

Stage four in the process of change is called the *action* step. This is the point at which the therapist joins with the client in identifying appropriate goals for early recovery and strategies for achieving these goals. It is at this step that we often see our clients in treatment for the first time. Of course, this is due to the fact that they generally need to go through the earlier steps in order to decide to seek help. At this stage, active participation in a Twelve Step program can greatly facilitate many of the changes the client will need to complete in early recovery. I will cover the therapeutic value of the Twelve Steps in the next chapter.

In the action stage we begin to explore the various resources the client brings to the change process, drawing the client into the treatment planning in a way that helps integrate the various aspects of his personality. What patterns of thought, belief systems, and coping strategies does the client habitually utilize? Which of these need to be challenged and altered, which strengthened? The therapist begins the methodical evaluation of the client's strengths, skills and weaknesses, becoming a partner with him or her in this process of exploration and change.

Of course, this is not the case with every client we meet who has entered treatment for the first time. Many forensic or court-mandated clients have entered treatment at the urging of significant others, simply to "get them off my back." Assuming that their presence in treatment implies they have reached the action step can be counterproductive. If the event or situation that led the client to enter treatment is not perceived by them as a motivational crisis, the therapists should be encouraged to help the clients perceive it that way. The client who is there simply to satisfy the urgings of his spouse or boss may need considerable work getting to the point where he or she recognizes the problem (contemplation) and is willing to do something about it (action). As with every case, we need to carefully assess the stage of motivation for each client. This is critical to the success of the intervention.

Once the individual has taken some action and made the desired changes, the fifth stage in the sequence is *maintenance*. I have found that this stage is another area in which a significant portion of the work of addictions counselors is needed. As William R. Miller (1989) put it, "It is not difficult to stop drinking; it's hard to *stay* sober" (p. 70). At this stage, the client begins to implement long-term alterations in broad areas of his or her life: where and with whom they associate, how they maintain health and manage stress, and other major areas. We call this making *lifestyle change*. This continuing evolution[15] takes the recovering addict or alcoholic on a journey away from relapse and addiction and toward a productive life. s at this point may involve significant cognitive behavioral restructuring of dysfunctional beliefs and strategies and assistance in evaluating relationships, occupations, avocations and other major elements in the client's life.

STAGE MODEL OF MOTIVATION

The final stage in the cycle is *relapse*, that ever present threat of a return to the destructive patterns that preceded treatment and recovery. As most therapists and counselors in the field of addictions counseling know, a return to use is not only possible, it is probable. Marlatt (1985), after reviewing the data, wrote, "...*relapse* is the most common outcome of alcoholism treatment" (p. 8). As negative as it sounds, this is critical to understand if you are treating addictions and other compulsive disorders. Regardless of how spectacular the client's growth during initial treatment, regardless of the profound depth of his insight into his problems and understanding of the principles of recovery, fully two-thirds of all who enter treatment will relapse.[16] It is an important part of the therapeutic relationship that the therapist does not judge the client based on a relapse episode. As pointed out so well in the work of Gorski and Miller (1982, 1986) and Marlatt (1985), the relapse episode is simply another opportunity for the recovering addict to learn better skills in sobriety. For this to occur, it *must* be reinforced by the addictions counselor.[17]

MOTIVATION AND TREATMENT PLANNING

If we look at Prochaska and DiClemente's model from the standpoint of treatment planning, it becomes apparent that problems may occur with certain types of interventions if applied at the wrong stage in the change cycle. For example, a person at the precontemplation stage will probably not respond well to a session designed to set up goals for "recovery." The client has yet to understand that there is anything for him or her to recover from!

While working for the U.S. Army in their Alcohol and Drug Abuse Prevention and Control Program (ADAPCP), a colleague, James Ronan, and I set up an extremely effective initial treatment program for new clients. Understanding that the majority of our clients were not self-referred – the bulk of them were identified for treatment following some drug or alcohol related incident – we needed an approach that maximally addressed the specific stage of motivation for change that each of these clients had achieved at the time of entry into the program. Because of the extremely high caseloads (far be it for me to complain about the Army's support in staffing the ADAPCP!), we also needed a treatment methodology that could effectively treat large numbers of clients in the most efficient manner possible. We decided on a group format, but needed one that would be flexible enough to accommodate the full range of clients from precontemplation to those who had gone beyond that step and were at various stages of looking for answers to their problems.

To address these needs, we designed a group called the Structured Substance Abuse Assessment/ group (SSAAI). This group proved so effective that it was subsequently adopted by the US Army V Corps as the primary initial treatment modality for new clients.[18] One of the elements that made this group so successful was the incorporation of the stages of motivation model into the treatment regimen. For a counselor in the field, knowledge of this model can prove a valuable and time-saving tool for treatment planning.

NOTES FOR CHAPTER 3

1. This problem is well-articulated by Smith and Wesson (1988) in their discussion of the rapid popularization of cocaine in the late 1960s and early 1970s in which one of the factors was a misunderstanding of the relationship between physical dependence and addiction.

2. He draws here from Saxe, Dougherty, and Esty, "The Effectiveness and Cost of Alcoholism Treatment" in Health Technology Case Study 22, Washington D.C.: Office of Tecnological Assessment, 1983.

3. Be forewarned that not all writers agree with the concept of addiction as a *disease*. One of the more controversial and outspoken is Fingarette (1988) in his book *Heavy Drinking: The Myth of Alcoholism as a Disease*.

4. Bateson (1972) notes that we "...must not expect the alcoholic to present a consistent picture" (p. 321), because his underlying epistemology (origin, nature, methods, and limits of knowledge) is full of error, causing self-contradictions and restrictions of his models of the world. This "error" is the result of alcohol and other drugs' effect on the alcoholic's brain.

5. In addition to Fingarette (1988) previously mentioned, another controversial book disputes the popularly accepted family disease concept of addiction. In *The Codependency Conspiracy* (Katz and Liu, 1991), the authors suggest, "By creating so many different disease characteristics, the codependence leaders offer a slot for everyone. We all must be codependents because we all fit at least one of the descriptions" (p. 16).

6. I do not endorse the use of illegal drugs, nor, ethically, should any mental health counselor. However, we need to be aware that there are certain subcultures who do not perceive use of certain drugs (marijuana, for example) as deviant and whose use forms an integral part of the social experience. For a member of one of these subcultures, a "return to social use" might include these drugs.

7. One excellent review of the basic theories and research on the controlled drinking issue can be found in Plum and Payne (1991, pp. 237-242).

8. Most professionals in the field today would agree that marijuana is addictive, both psychologically and physically. The discussion can become heated, however, with lay persons or during early recovery groups.

9. Contrary to the belief of many in self-help recovery programs, the evidence points towards a need to deal with both compulsions simultaneously. Washington (1989), for example, has identified sexual triggers to relapse in cocaine addicted clients with associated sexual compulsions. If the sexual compulsion remains untreated, the tendency to relapse becomes significantly greater.

10. Videotapes of this seminar are available through the Southern Institute of Neuro-Linguistic Programming, P.O. Box 533, Indian Rocks Beach, FL 33535, (813) 596-4891. Dilts reiterates this more recently in his book *Changing Belief Systems with NLP* (Dilts 1990, p. 11).

11. Bateson (1971) likens the internal battle to a variation of the Cartesian dualism (division between the Mind and Matter). He notes the alcoholic battles between conscious will (will-power) and "the remainder of the personality". It is a struggle between his "pride" ("I can resist the bottle") and his "other" self in a symmetrical relationship which is prone to escalation of the problem.

12. In fact, Bateson (1971) suggests that "It is possible...that 'bottom' is reached many times by any given individual; that 'bottom' is a spell of panic which provides a favorable moment for change, but not a moment at which change is inevitable" (pp. 329-330). This is what I meant earlier by "the window is open". While open, the client is more vulnerable to the influence of the therapist and others in his or her life; however, through the mechanisms of denial, the door may close again quite abruptly. As Bateson observes, "The attempt to change the alcoholic in a period between such moments of panic is unlikely to succeed" (p. 330).

13. Bill W., one of the founders of AA and the author of *Twelve Steps and Twelve Traditions*, was convinced that this sharing of personal stories was the foundation of the recovery alcoholics found in AA. He wrote, "By going back in our drinking histories, we could show that years before we realized it we were out of control, that our drinking even then was no mere habit, that it was indeed the beginning of a fatal progression" (p. 23). This form of "educating" the newcomer is often called "planting the seed". Wrote

Bill W., "It was then discovered that when one alcoholic had planted in the mind of another the true nature of his malady, that person could never be the same again. Following every spree, he would say to himself, 'Maybe those A.A.'s were right....'" (p. 23).

14. It is important to note that ambivalence and denial can return at any time during or after treatment. It often takes the form of *euphoric recall* wherein the client begins to actively imagine past pleasant use experiences. These fantasies often precede a return to use and can be seen as a "red flag" or a relapse warning sign. These issues are thoroughly covered in Volume II of this series, *Sobriety Demystified: Staying Clean and Sober with NLP and CBT*, currently pending publication.

15. One of the best descriptions of the ongoing process of recovery can be found in the books by Gorski and Miller (1982, 1986). They are worthwhile reading for anyone involved in addictions counseling or recovery.

16. According to Miller (1989), depending on the source, the statistics for relapse run anywhere from 60% to 90%!

17. I cover this process in great detail in Volume II of this series, *Sobriety Demystified: Staying Clean and Sober with NLP and CBT*, currently pending publication.

18. The complete SSAAI program is currently being published by Pegasus Press, Fairbanks, Alaska. Inquiries can be sent to James D. Ronan, Jr., c/o Kelsey & Co Publishing.

THE TWELVE STEPS*

1. We admitted we were powerless over alcohol-that our lives had become, unmanageable.

2. Came to believe that a Power greater than ourselves could restore us to sanity.

3. Made a decision to turn our will and our lives over to the care of God *as we understood Him.*

4. Made a searching and fearless moral inventory of ourselves.

5. Admitted to God, to ourselves and to another human being the exact nature of our wrongs.

6. Were entirely ready to have God remove all these defects of character.

7. Humbly asked Him to remove our shortcomings.

8. Made a list of all persons we had harmed, and became ready to make amends to them all.

9. Made direct amends to such people wherever possible, except where to do so would injure them or others.

10. Continued to take personal inventory and when we were wrong promptly admitted it.

11. Sought through prayer and meditation to improve our conscious contact with God *as we understood Him,* praying only for knowledge of His will for us and the power to carry that out.

12. Having had a spiritual awakening as a result of these Steps, we tried to carry this message to alcoholics, and to practice these principles in all our affairs.

*The Twelve Steps are reprinted with permission of Alcoholics Anonymous World Services, Inc. Permission to reprint this material does not mean that A.A. has reviewed or approved the contents of this publication, nor that A.A. agrees with the views expressed herein. A.A. is a program of recovery from alcoholism—use of the Twelve Steps in connection with programs and activities which are patterned after A.A., but which address other problems, does not imply otherwise.

TWELVE STEP PROGRAMS

4

...some fifty years ago,

an organization was born under

the unlikely leadership of a group of

...hopeless' drunks, and given an equally

unlikely name: Alcoholics Anonymous. The most

startling thing about this group, however,

wasn't its name or its leadership. It was

simply that it appeared to work

(Rogers and McMillin 1989, p. 11).

Alcoholics Anonymous, Al-Anon, Narcotics Anonymous, and the many other Twelve Step programs are the single most often used form of treatment for individuals suffering from addictive disorders in the United States today (Blum & Payne, 1991). Born of the frustration of two chronic alcoholics, Alcoholics Anonymous had a slow beginning. But today, even with the tremendous interest and growth in the field of addictions counseling, "...AA is reaching approximately two-thirds as many alcoholics as all of the hospitals, clinics, and treatment centers combined, and now is regarded by many as the single most effective institution for dealing with alcoholism" (Blum & Payne, 1991, p. 46).

Is AA as effective as the claims? Although difficult to research due to the tradition of anonymity, the General Services Office of Alcoholics Anonymous has published several studies done on its members. Recently they concluded that, of members who are attending meetings, participants with one year of sobriety have about a 40 percent chance of remaining sober at least one more year. Those with five years sobriety have at least a 90 percent probability of remaining sober another year.[1] These statistics rate very favorably compared with the results of other treatment methodologies!

Harold Swift (1984) is the administrator of the Hazelden Foundation, the largest publishers of recovery literature in the world. He has expressed concern that the philosophy and methods of Alcoholics Anonymous are generally not very well understood by either the public or many health care professionals. This is significant, because for those in the field of addictions counseling, familiarity with the Twelve Step Programs can be extremely useful.

Because so many addicted clients are either members or will come into contact with members of Twelve Step programs, the ability to talk cogently with them about their experiences can be an extremely important part of the therapeutic relationship. The therapist can use knowledge of the program to gain and maintain rapport with clients already in or entering recovery through one of the Twelve Step programs. These programs also offer a ready referral source for long-term follow-up to help maintain the therapeutic gains of compulsive or chemically dependent clients.

In addition to positive benefits of familiarity with the Twelve Step programs, certain misunderstandings regarding AA are counterproductive for both the client and therapist. Swift (1984) points out that to the uninformed public, AA is a group of people who simply tell the alcoholic to stop drinking. In actuality, no one in AA will tell the alcoholic to stop drinking. AA believes that the decision to stop drinking (or using any mood-altering drugs or compulsive disorders) should be entirely left up to the individual. This belief is one of the cornerstones of an organization built on "one alcoholic talking to another" to help one another stay sober another 24 hours.

THE MEETING

For counselors who have never attended a Twelve Step meeting, it is useful to have a general understanding of what goes on. The public has been exposed to many a meeting in the media over the last few years, and there are a number of pamphlets available that describe the program and what the newcomer can expect.[2] However, nothing can take the place of actually attending an open meeting. I strongly recommend that any health care professional dealing with addiction attend open Twelve Step meetings and become fully acquainted with the processes.

THE MEETING

A meeting usually begins with the *secretary* of the meeting (all positions in AA at the local level are unpaid and voluntary) asking for a moment of silence followed by the "Serenity Prayer." Then there is a reading of the preamble, the Twelve Steps and Twelve Traditions. From the introductory preamble comes:

Rarely have we seen a person fail who has thoroughly followed our path. Those who do not recover are people who cannot or will not completely give themselves to this simple program...(Alcoholics Anonymous, 1976, p. 58).

Regardless of the program, whether AA, Gamblers Anonymous, Narcotics Anonymous, Cocaine Anonymous, etc., each meeting will start with some variation of the above process. The next step depends upon the type of meeting. Either a *speaker* is introduced, a person in recovery who will talk about "how it was, what happened, and how it is now." If it is not a speakers meeting, the *chairperson* will introduce a discussion topic. Some meetings focus on the study of the Twelve Steps and Twelve Traditions or on readings from the "Big Book".

There are different "styles" of meetings. During some, people are called upon to speak about their own experiences, thoughts and feelings about the topic or the speaker's story. At other meetings, members raise their hands to be called upon to share. In others, participants stand and introduce themselves, then share their thoughts. There were meetings in Germany I had the pleasure of attending where members "signed in" prior to the beginning of the meeting if they wanted to share.

The basic form of meetings is constant, whether in Germany, Italy, England, etc. For those in recovery who travel, it is kind of like the "McDonalds phenomenon": regardless of where you go in the world, in almost every major city you can order yourself a "Big Mac." Of course, you have to order it in a different language and pay for it with a different currency, but a "Big Mac" it is, none-the-less. During the last few years, with the opening up of the "iron curtain," we now have meetings of Alcoholics Anonymous in Moscow and Leningrad!

At the conclusion of the meeting, participants typically will stand, join hands, recite the Lord's Prayer, and chant a version of "Keep coming back; it works!" What often follows is a social gathering at a local restaurant for coffee and talk. As this *fellowship* of men and women broadens and strengthens, other clean and sober activities are planned, and members network amongst themselves in support of ongoing recovery.

A BRIEF HISTORY

The two founders of AA were themselves products of the Temperance Movement, Prohibition (and it's eventual repeal), World War I, and the "Great Crash" of the New York Stock Market. They also brought with them the biases and beliefs of their generation as well as their personal backgrounds. Bill W. was a stockbroker who lost everything in "the crash." Bob S. was a physician who had been unable to maintain his practice due to his drinking. Both had repeatedly tried to quit drinking. Dr. Bob had even tried using the Oxford Group[3] parlor meetings unsuccessfully to quit his obsession. Bill W. was institutionalized in locked psychiatric wards (common treatment in those days) several times without any lasting results. In fact, it was during intense withdrawals while institutionalized following his last binge that Bill W. had what he later called the *spiritual awakening* that precipitated his core beliefs about recovery. Dr. Bob brought with him the format and experiences of the Oxford Group to their eventual meetings.

One weekend in May, 1935, Bill W., struggling to keep himself from drinking while on a business trip, decided to use a technique he had stumbled upon that seemed to help keep him sober during the difficult times. Through the local clergy he was able to set up a meeting with another "unfortunate alcoholic." That meeting not only kept both Bill W. and Dr. Bob sober another 24 hours, it heralded the beginnings of a relationship that formed the foundation for a new approach to working with the suffering alcoholic. Although many years and tremendous struggles separated that meeting from the actual formation of the organization now known as Alcoholics Anonymous, that first meeting has been heralded as the origin of the fellowship.

WHY IT WORKS

There are a number of factors that help to explain the success of Twelve Step programs. From its inception, AA appeared to more clearly address the biopsychosocial nature of alcoholism than any previous forms of treatment, and it continues to this day to be a model form of recovery[4]. What follows are descriptions of how AA and the other Twelve Step programs impact their members lives. The Twelve Step recovery process offers prescriptions for recovery from physical addiction and psychological distress, as well as for social reintegration, and spiritual growth.

PRESCRIPTION FOR PHYSICAL ADDICTION

In the backlash of the repeal of prohibition, AA was founded on the principle that alcoholism is a disease of the body. Labeled an "allergy," AA's proponents cited physicians whose testimony clearly placed the origins of the problem within the body of the alcoholic. Echoing the American Disease model, this belief requires absolute abstinence before treatment can commence.

As a prescription for recovery from physical addiction, there is no more effective remedy than abstention! However, this is the very root of the addict's problem: how to stop and stay stopped. Historically, the prohibitionist and temperance movements had been preaching abstinence for years without widespread or lasting success. AA had to come up with more than this obvious solution.

PRESCRIPTION FOR PSYCHOLOGICAL DISTRESS

Although viewed as a disease of the body, AA's founders clearly understood the role of the *mind* in the addictive process. "The Big Book" speaks to this early in the second chapter. In discussing the "solution," it points out that if an alcoholic could resist the first drink, he would never set the "terrible cycle" in motion. "Therefore, the main problem of the alcoholic centers in his mind, rather than his body"[5] (p. 23), which we know will begin to recover with continued abstinence. This belief opens the door to exploration of emotional and psychological aspects of the alcoholic's life. By focusing on abstinence first, followed by thorough self exploration, we now have a foundation for the sweeping lifestyle changes necessary for recovery.

PRESCRIPTION FOR SOCIAL REINTEGRATION

An addict or alcoholic does not become addicted in a void. Every person who has contact with the addict is affected by the disease. A fundamental part of recovery in AA has to do with the *fellowship*, the organization of men and women whose purpose is to stay sober. The fellowship is more than a group of people simply going to meetings. It encourages open and honest sharing of oneself, good and bad, with other members of the program. The fellowship also supports two basic themes of AA: *service* and *sponsorship*. Working with other addicts by serving within the organization or sponsoring new and continuing members is a basic component of the Twelve Step programs.

These themes are also reflected in the Twelfth Step, as we will see in a the following section.

Through service, newcomers are invited to participate with setting up the meeting place, making coffee, and cleaning up afterwards. As members continue with the program, they are invited to "chair" and to "secretary" meetings. Service continues with elected appointments to local and national bodies, participation on local telephone crisis and hot lines, and in *Twelve-Stepping*: going out to suffering alcoholics/addicts and talking with them about the program.

Sponsorship occurs when one sober member begins to guide another member through the Twelve Steps, one at a time. This intense, personal interaction is a cornerstone of the Twelve Step programs. It encourages the addict/alcoholic to come "out of hiding" and supplies "motivation" to continue to progress along the Steps. Gorski (1989) suggests that service and sponsorship work by pulling the individual out of what he calls "addictive self-centeredness".

PRESCRIPTION FOR SPIRITUAL GROWTH

Although it is called a "spiritual program'" AA is not a religious organization. The Big Book discusses the spiritual aspect of the program in some detail. This reflects the bias born of experience of the founders of AA who saw a *spiritual awakening* as the essential component to recovery. There are many examples of this theme throughout the Twelve Step literature. For example, the following excerpt from the "Big Book" is attributed to Dr. Carl Jung:

The doctor said: "You have the mind of a chronic alcoholic. I have never seen one single case recover, where that state of mind existed to the extent that it does in you." Our friend felt as though the gates of hell had closed on him with a clang.

He said to the doctor, "Is there no exception?"

"Yes," replied the doctor, "there is. Exceptions to cases such as yours have been occurring since early times. Here and there, once in a while, alcoholics have had what are called vital spiritual experiences. To me these occurrences are phenomena. They appear to be in the nature of huge emotional displacements and rearrangements. Ideas, emotions, and attitudes which were once the guiding forces of the lives of these men are suddenly cast to one side, and a completely new set of conceptions and motives begin to dominate them (p. 27).

The book goes on to describe that simple religious conviction is not enough for the "conversion" described by Dr. Jung. It is more establishing a *personal relationship* with God or some other "Higher Power" of the addict's own choosing. They point out, however, that "We have no desire to convince anyone that there is only one way by which faith can be acquired" (p. 28), and conclude that religious affiliation is not even necessary for the changes to occur. Regardless of the words used, these descriptions have a common central theme: the spiritual "awakening", the "vital spiritual experience", or "conversion" all imply some dramatic cognitive transformation.

It is not unusual for clients in recovery and even the counselors who work with them to struggle with the Twelve Step concept of spirituality. It is an issue that needs to be honestly addressed by anyone working within the recovering community. It is particularly important for counselors working with cognitive-behavioral technologies to be able to address this issue with their clients.

We are fortunate that, because this is such an important element of the Twelve Step programs, there is a significant body of writings on the subject. Gorski (1989) is particularly well received by the recovering community for his work with relapse prevention. In one work well suited to our discussion he shares his own concept of spirituality and how it differs from mainstream AA. He calls it *rational spirituality* and writes, "I believe that spiritual truth and rational truth are the same thing; that they are different paths to the same point, using different faculties of the creative mind" (p. 140).

Regardless of the counselor's own interpretations, however, we all need to recognize that progression along a spiritual path is fundamental to Twelve Step programs. As the addict, alcoholic, or compulsive sufferer starts working through the steps, the changes leading to the spiritual awakening begin. It may be the magnitude of these changes that makes AA work for so many. In a recent book, Sikorsky (1990) published a letter to Dr. Carl Jung from Bill W. In the letter, Bill described the personal vital spiritual experience that precipitated his recovery from alcoholism. He wrote, "...most conversion experiences, whatever their variety, do have a common denominator of ego collapse at depth" (p. 12). He described how he then sought to *force* this event on other alcoholics by convincing them of their hopeless situation and compelling them to face an "impossible dilemma" centered on their powerlessness over alcohol. He describes how this became one of the fundamental precepts of AA, saying, "In the wake of my spiritual experience, there came a vision of a society of alcoholics, each identifying with and transmitting his experience to the next — chain style. If each sufferer were to carry the news of the scientific hopelessness of alcoholism to each new prospect, he might be able to lay every newcomer wide open to a transforming spiritual experience. This concept proved to be the foundation of such success as Alcoholics Anonymous has since achieved" (p. 12).

At its core, then, AA is a spiritual program. We will explore in the section that follows just how the Twelve Steps of AA lead to this "spiritual awakening." Obviously, change as fundamental as those described by Carl Jung and Bill W. will have dramatic effects on a person. When we work with our addicted clients, this type of change is often exactly what we are after.

LOGICAL LEVELS OF CHANGE MODEL

One excellent model of change proposed by Dilts (1990) fits well with what occurs during the Twelve Step recovery process. He describes how changes occur in systems in general and in humans in particular. His model shows how these changes occur at various "logical levels" of human functioning. The more levels a change affects, the more profound will be the consequences of the change.

In Dilts' model, change at the highest level of human functioning occurs at the *spiritual* level. Such a change will result in consequential changes in each of the five subsequent levels beneath it. In descending order, they are *identity*, *beliefs* and *values*, *capabilities*, *behaviors*, and *environment*. Using this cognitive model as a guide, then, anyone progressing through the Twelve Step program to this "spiritual awakening" will experience fundamental changes in self-concept and core beliefs and values. In addition, they will begin to alter what they can and will do, and we will also find changes in the places they frequent, the friends they keep and the activities they are involved with. We usually call such changes *lifestyle change*.

HOW IT WORKS

It is generally accepted that the founders of AA were strongly influenced by a popular Christian movement of that time called the Oxford Group. Founded by an evangelical minister from Allentown, PA, Frank Buchman established his program at Oxford University in 1921. Meeting with undergraduates, Buchman's goal was to help people practice a more Christian oriented and moral life. His non-denominational movement also caught on in the United States, where people would meet informally in parlors and living rooms to participate in groups that were learning and practicing Buchman's principles.

A.A.'s Twelve Steps are a group of principles, spiritual in their nature, which, if practiced as a way of life, can expel the obsession to drink and enable the sufferer to become happily and usefully whole (Twelve Steps and Twelve Traditions, 1976, p. 15).

As we explore the Twelve Steps, it will become clear that Buchman's principles formed the inspiration for the structure of AA meetings. These principles included 1) unconditional surrender of the human will to the will of God, 2) taking a personal moral inventory, 3) sharing confessions with others in meetings, 4) making amends to those harmed, and 5) working with others needing help.[6] Both Bill W. and Dr. Bob attended these meetings and incorporated these principles into their Twelve Step program.

THE TWELVE STEPS

What follows are the Twelve Steps originated by Alcoholics Anonymous and universally applied in all the Twelve Step programs. My analysis and interpretation of these Steps is my own and has not been sanctioned by Alcoholics Anonymous. In keeping with the Twelve Traditions, AA does not endorse nor does it have an opinion on outside issues or enterprises such as this book.[7]

STEP ONE

"We admitted we were powerless over (alcohol, drugs, our emotions, food, gambling[8]) – that our lives had become unmanageable."

In the First Step, we are introduced to two remarkable aspects of the Twelve Step programs. The very first word in this step underscores one of the major contributions this program has had to the millions who suffer from compulsive disorders. As addiction develops, one of the characteristic symptoms is the tendency to isolate oneself as a way of insulating the dysfunctional internal system from external reminders of the pain and suffering. This sense of loneliness eventually pervades all aspects of the addict's life. The use of the plural *we* in the Twelve Steps underscores, especially to the newcomer, that he or she is not alone. It shows that others have gone before and have suffered as have they. From the onset, new members are surrounded by people just like themselves; others who have similar stories, have fought similar battles, and who, with the support of members in the fellowship, are now following a path of recovery. This first word helps to break down the devastating sense of uniqueness and isolation caused by the addict's struggles with the problem.

The second noteworthy aspect of this and all the following steps is that they are expressed *in the past tense*. In my first book there is an extensive discussion about the difference between the *surface structure* (spoken or written language) and the *deep structure* (the semantic origins of the words and phrases)[9]. In the Twelve Steps, we have a situation where the surface structure a person hears or reads triggers a deep structure understanding, a portion of which occurs at the unconscious level, of the meaning of the phrase. The fact that each step is expressed in the past tense linguistically implies that the step *has already been taken*.

In the case of the First Step, I read or hear the surface structure "We admitted to ourselves...", and, whether or not it is *true*, understand it to be a *fait accompli*. This cognitive process serves to positively reinforce behaviors congruent with having already taken the steps. As newcomers read, study, learn, and recite these steps, they begin to unconsciously assimilate them into their everyday lives. Of course, this is a well-documented cognitive-behavioral therapy technique: the repetitive recitation of statements such as these will alter a persons thoughts, feelings and behaviors.

There is another noteworthy aspect of the First Step. It is the only Step in which the "motivating problem" (i.e., alcohol, drugs, food, etc.) is mentioned. This clearly demonstrates a primary curative aspect of the Twelve Step program: the focus is not on the problem, but rather on the solution. In addition, intrinsic to this step is a primary principle of Twelve Step programs known as *rigorous honesty*. Addicts must admit to the fullest extent the nature of their problems. This step forces them to start that process.

The First Step delineates two distinct aspects of addiction: *powerlessness* and *unmanageability*. By simply admitting to these debilitating problems, an addict takes the first step to initiate a process of recovery from the destructive disease that has dominated and corrupted his life.

One thing addiction fosters is a tendency to ignore the consequences of the compulsive behavior. The addict believes – and is quite willing to tell anyone else – that he or she can handle the problem. "I can stop any time I want," they say, or, "I'll never drink or use that much again!" The tragedy is that they believe these statements, even in the face of repeated failures to control their use patterns. Of course, this is one of the primary symptoms of denial. However, when they speak the line, "We admitted we were powerless over (alcohol, drugs, sex and love, gambling, etc.)....," they are practicing an affirmation of reality which they have been unable to accept in the past. This admission of powerlessness becomes the foundation of their final surrender[10] to the addiction.

By admitting powerlessness over the problem, the sufferer takes the first step toward what Bill W. called a "transforming spiritual experience." In the *Twelve Steps and Twelve Traditions*, he writes, "The principle that we shall find no enduring strength until we first admit complete defeat is the main taproot from which our whole Society has sprung" (p. 22). For many, this admission heralds the genesis of therapeutic change. In taking the First Step, the addict must *consciously* become aware of and acknowledge the problem. Since denial previously prevented this conscious awareness, taking this step is a positive demonstration of movement through that denial. In terms of the stage model of motivation described in Chapter 3, this step represents the transition from *precontemplation* to the *contemplation* stage of change.

In a fundamental way, by recognizing his powerlessness over the addiction, the addict admits *defeat*. Prior to this admission, addicts suffer under the illusion that they can somehow regain control over their use of drugs, alcohol or compulsive behavior. It is as if they have two distinct identities residing inside. One aspect knows the addict is powerless, has "collected the proof" over time and urgently wants the individual to quit the behavior once and for all. The other aspect remembers only the relief and/or pleasure produced by the behavior, the drinking or drugging. This second part also strongly believes that there is *no other way* to achieve these results, and so the two parts of the personality constantly "wage battle" within the addict.[11] In cognitive-behavioral terms, this step forces into the open this ongoing internal conflict between disparate belief systems. It forces the individual to use logical, sequential, cause-and-effect thinking to come to terms with both parts of this step.

The second part of this step has to do with recognizing the unmanageability of life as a result of the addiction. Many addicts do get to the point that they can recognize their powerlessness over their compulsion. At that point, it is easy to say, "Well, then I simply need to quit." However, what they often don't recognize — and this again is due to the process of denial — is the shambles their lives have become. Addiction affects the *whole* person: health deteriorates, mental functioning is interfered with, friendships dissolve, there is often loss of jobs, family, material things, and the less tangible self-respect, identity, and spirituality. By admitting and repeatedly affirming that one's life has become unmanageable, the addict continues to impact his or her denial. This process also paves the way for the individual to finally reach out, to ask for help, and to accept the need to make significant changes in his or her life well beyond simply "quitting."

One final aspect of this step has to do with the logical level of change required in order to take it. Using Dilts' (1990) model, this step occurs at the level of a person's capabilities. This step tells the individual "I can't control my drinking, and I can't control my life." By taking this step, the addict can significantly impact the levels of functioning below that level. The first level is *behavior*. This includes overt behaviors as well as conscious and unconscious strategies used to decide whether or not to drink. The next level is *environment*. We all enjoy a certain amount of control over both our internal and external environments. For example, we can control our internal equilibrium by choosing not to introduce mood-altering chemicals or behaviors into the system. In a similar way, addicts in recovery can control their external equilibrium by staying away from "slippery playthings, playfriends, and playplaces."

STEP TWO

> *"Came to believe that a Power*
> *greater than ourselves*
> *could restore us to sanity."*

Embedded within this statement is a powerful *linguistic presupposition*. This is a surface structure statement which implies at the deep structure that something must be true. In this case, for the sentence to make sense, the presupposition that the speaker has *lost his sanity*[12] must be true. When an addict reads this step, he or she responds at a deep level to this linguistic form. It acknowledges and affirms the insanity of the disease. It confirms the addict's personal experiences with the devastating power of the drug, the alcohol, or the compulsion and the resulting feelings of absolute loss of control over all aspects of life. The message is that all the insanity, the crazy ways of thinking and acting were very real. "Yes," it says, "you *were* insane, but now all that is over."

This step is imbued with hope. With this step, addicts embrace the possibility that *something* might finally work to change their lives. Goodness knows, they have struggled long and hard to make these changes themselves without success. When the alcoholic or addict finally takes this step, there is almost always an overwhelming sense of relief. After months and years of anguish over the feeling of *hopelessness* — "I *can't* quit. I'll *never* regain control over my life." — , the addict now begins to believe that change is possible and that there is hope after all.

In spite of the tone of the language, this is not a "religious" step. Nor is it an affirmation or embracing of any specific religious dogma. In fact, the *Twelve Steps and Twelve Traditions* states very clearly, "First, Alcoholics Anonymous does not demand that you believe anything. All of its Twelve Steps are but suggestions. Second, to get sober and to stay sober, you don't have to swallow all of Step Two right now, [and] Third, all you really need is a truly open mind" (p. 26).

Rather than espousing religiosity, Step Two suggests a move toward the spiritual healing alluded to by Jung and reported by Bill W. This cognitive transformation appears to take place most easily when the individual reaches out for help. Blum and Payne (1991) write, "… an inner change begins when the individual begins to look beyond the self for insight, encouragement, and help" (p. 42). This external *power greater than ourselves* can take many different forms. For those with a belief in God, regardless of the sect or denomination, this step reaffirms their faith. Others who consider themselves "nonreligious," find that it can mark the beginning of the process of identifying and embracing a "spiritual advisor." For some, it is simply recognizing that there are others — therapists, counselors, physicians, AA or NA members or Twelve Step sponsors can all be perceived as "Higher Powers" — who know more about addiction and recovery than they do.[13]

I have long been intrigued by similarities between Twelve Step member's use of a "Higher Power" and one of the old NLP axioms (coming from Erickson, of course) to "Trust your unconscious mind." In a later step, we are encouraged to continue to improve this contact through prayer and meditation. This process might be considered parallel to a client working to develop a "worthy advisor" or other hypnotic resource such as a *meta part*.

For those recovering from addiction through the Twelve Step programs, the belief in a healing power outside oneself has an integrative effect. While reinforcing the process of internal change begun in Step One, it focuses the addict's attention away from the internal conflict between the addicted-self and the sober-self and towards a healthy trust in the experience and help of others. Over time, the reliance on the guidance of a "Higher Power" eventually replaces the habitual internal warring between parts with a *meta part* or internal advisor which can be communicated with through prayer or meditation. If there is difficulty identifying this advisor, all the AA participant needs to do is listen to others talk about their experiences during the meetings. This provides one with a model to emulate as he embarks on the road back to sanity.

The Second Step involves change at a higher level of functioning in Dilt's model of change than Step One. Rather than emphasizing semiconscious patterns of *behavior*, this step directly impacts *belief systems*. Since it is in great measure our beliefs that motivate us and provide the impetus to change and grow (or *not*!), the process of taking this step has even farther reaching consequences than Step One. This new belief "gives permission" to reach out for assistance in dealing with the problem and all that it has produced in the addict's life. In changing at the level of belief, we discover that each of the levels of functioning beneath also change: capabilities, behaviors, and environment. From the stage model of motivation, this step also represents the next level up. In Step Two, the addict moves from *contemplation* to *determination*. With hope for change comes the resolve to make it happen. It makes sense, then that the next step moves the person to the *action* stage in the model.

STEP THREE

"Made a decision to turn
our will and our lives
over to the care of God
as we understood him."

One of the hallmarks of addiction is an obsession with the issue of *control*. From the earliest minor problems that arise as a result of the addiction, the person has struggled to maintain (and in the end, simply to regain) some control over the substance or behavior. With unbelievable tenacity, the addict repeatedly attempts to control the compulsion through willpower. Step Three asks the addict to ultimately *give up all control*. This is so fundamentally opposed to the direction of the struggle up to that point that it requires a major shift in his sense of identity.

Step Three is an action step that naturally follows the work accomplished at Step Two. It proposes that, since the addict now believes in a Higher Power, it is time to put some faith in that belief. This goes beyond simply restructuring a few strategies or revising belief systems. In taking this step, a person must actually "evolve". This form of change impacts the *core* of the individual, the "beingness" or "who I am" at the center of each one of us. By turning his "will and life" over to a Higher Power, the addict must let go his ego entirely. In Dilts' model of logical levels of change, such evolution occurs at the level of human functioning just short of spiritual change.

Like the previous step, this step forces addicts to go "outside" themselves and begin to explore standards of conduct that are more socially acceptable than the behavior motivated by distorted addictive thought. Blum and Payne (1991) state, "In practical terms, this step means the willingness to relinquish old attitudes and patterns of living that have produced pain and disappointment, and to adopt new attitudes and patterns as an act of faith" (p. 42).

We must remember, however, that we are dealing with a damaged brain in a newly recovering addict. It is not unreasonable to ask, then, where do these new standards of conduct come from? The answer can be found in the slogans, the meetings and the fellowship of the Twelve Step programs. Each of these play a critical role in guiding the individual towards more healthy and productive perceptions, attitudes and beliefs. During the meetings, while listening to others describe "how it was, what happened, and how it is now", the addict begin to understand exactly what the old attitudes and patterns were and what the new attitudes and patterns need to be. The many slogans of the program reinforce this fragile newly developing identity. "Think, think, think" and "One day at a time" are often posted in the meeting hall. Participants recite the *serenity prayer*[14] during the meeting, and some even carry it on a key chain or a card in wallet or purse. Fulfilling one aspect of the fellowship, the sponsor models appropriate action and guides members through each of the steps. In all of these cases, the addict is coached and reminded as to what is "right action" and "healthy thought and behavior."

When we look at the progression of the first three steps, we see that each requires change at consecutively higher levels of human functioning. Step One required change at the level of a person's *capabilities*. It moves the addict from denial to contemplation of the problem. Step Two asks for alterations in the addict's *beliefs* and *values*. Here he gains the hope needed to make the decision to change. At Step Three, addicts must reorganize their sense of self, their *identity*, in order to fulfill the change. This step initiates action towards the lifestyle changes needed to become clean and sober. It is clearly more than chance that this program results in a spiritual awakening. By the time they take the Third Step, recovering addicts have been carefully prepared to experience such an event.

Using the stage model of motivation, we can see the systematic progression through each of the first three steps towards change. The next six steps of the Twelve

Step program alternate between *contemplation*, *determination*, and *action*. The last three steps are *maintenance* steps.

STEP FOUR

*"Made a searching and fearless
moral inventory of ourselves."*

When worked well, the focus of this step is on the *here and now*. Unlike traditional psychotherapy which strives to understand a person based on his or her past, this step utilizes a simple task to orient Twelve Step members to the specific goal of self evaluation. Step Four asks those in the program to list their strengths and weaknesses, the "raw materials" so to speak, that they are bringing into recovery. This is obviously a *contemplation* step. However, they are encouraged to move on to de*termination* by writing their list. Of course, just because this sounds simple doesn't mean that it is *easy*! Many individuals faced with this task for the first time find themselves almost paralyzed by the enormity of the project.

In practical terms, this step also requires members to start evaluating themselves using a basic moral code of "good" and "bad" or "right" and "wrong." Because of this, it cannot be initiated too early in the recovery process when the addict's thoughts are likely to be influenced by the overly distorted thought processes of a drug-clouded brain. It requires a fairly "clear" and "level head" to make such distinctions. In this step, Gorski (1989) says addicts ask questions like: "Is how I'm conducting my life good for me or bad for me? Is it helping me or hurting me...[and] people I love" (p. 116)? There is a healthy

*SEARCHING AND FEARLESS
MORAL INVENTORY*

balance in this step. It asks the person to list both strengths and weaknesses, their productive and destructive patterns of mood, thought, and behavior.

One important aspect of this step is that it focuses on *personal attributes*. This directs attention away from the alcohol and other drugs or compulsive behaviors. This means one can no longer use the addiction as an excuse for inappropriate behaviors or as a reason for failure. As was explained previously, Twelve Step programs do not view alcoholism or addiction as a psychological or moral disease, but rather as a physical disease that disrupts a person's ability to make healthy and rational decisions. As they begin working through the Twelve Steps, especially with this step and those that follow, recovering addicts move towards *taking responsibility* for their moral and emotional being. This step sets the tone for healthy psychological recovery.

While continuing and deepening the identity work initiated in the previous step, Step Four strongly impacts the participant's belief systems. As part of the inventory, for example, they are encouraged to explore the opposing concepts of pride and humility. This is a critical area, for addicts have spent the majority of their addicted life building belief systems that support a totally self-absorbed lifestyle. The Second and Third Steps focused them towards accepting a Higher Power. However, the concept of a Higher Power is contrary to an addict's egocentric sense of self-importance and the wall of beliefs sustaining this perception. Step Four asks them to reconsider the beliefs that support the perception of being different or special by labeling these beliefs *pride*. As the beliefs are systematically challenged, they begin to feel vulnerable. Unable to continue to act irresponsibly or feel impervious to others, they begin to become aware of the consequences of what they say and do and the effects the people they socialize with have on their lives. In a very positive and healthy way, this forces addicts to reassess how they relate to the world and re-evaluate their own beliefs about who they are.

STEP FIVE

*"Admitted to God, to ourselves,
and to another human being
the exact nature of our wrongs."*

The inspiration for this step can be traced directly to the AA founders' experiences with the Oxford Groups[15]. Public confessions were an important part of the Oxford Group ritual during their parlor meetings and "house parties." In a way, this sharing might be considered similar to formal Catholic confession, and the process of declaration carries with it an implied belief in absolution.

In Step Five, another *action* step, Twelve Step members "get honest" with themselves and others and concede past wrong-doings. The result is often a cathartic sense of relief. Suddenly there is no longer the need to maintain the vast network of lies woven to protect the addiction. By sharing their deep *secrets*, the terrible deeds resulting from the insanity of the disease, with another trusted individual, they are relieved to find that they are not *judged*. Quite the contrary, they discover they are not alone, that they are far more similar to the vast numbers of others in recovery than they are different. The exchange between the addict and "another human being" is one of the most intimate experiences many in recovery have ever had. Of course, it is frightening because of the natural concerns about acceptance and vulnerability; however, it has the potential to be an incredibly powerful experience.

In harmony with the previous steps, this step suggests that the addicts begin by communicating with the god of their understanding. This initial communion is often a form of prayer or meditation. It is a "rehearsal" of sorts for what is to follow. This reinforces an important integral part of the Twelve Step recovery process: communication with one's Higher Power. However conceptualized, the members of Twelve Step programs are regularly asked to practice being open to the process of praying or meditating for guidance from this source "outside" themselves. Since this step requires that they become aware of and share experiences drawn from the logical levels of their behaviors, capabilities, and beliefs, it is a dramatic step towards the spiritual awakening reported by many who find recovery in these programs.

Step Five helps break down many of the barriers built up over years of self-destructive abuse. The isolation and feelings of worthlessness begin to dissipate as participants experience acceptance for past transgressions and acknowledge their place amongst others with similar pasts. Many addicts find, perhaps for the first time in their lives, an experience of peace both within themselves and with others.

It is usually strongly suggested that this sharing with "another human being" be with a Twelve Step sponsor or with a counselor well versed in recovery issues. To simply share the results of the Fourth Step inventory indiscriminately would be foolhardy. This is an extremely vulnerable time for a person in recovery. The addict has unveiled himself and sits naked and exposed.

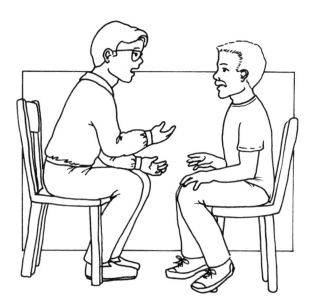

SHARING THE FIFTH STEP

He is terrified at that point of being judged and humili-
ated. At the moment of the sharing, he needs feedback
of a sensitive nature. This feedback should be consistent, accepting, and to the point. For the sponsor who
has "been there", it is easy to convey the message of
acceptance. For the counselor who has seen it so many
before, the same is true. This is the essence of *caring*,
and it may be an unfamiliar response to the addict who
has consistently acted in ways that drive others away.
In fact, it is this response that often cracks the insula-
tion and other barriers that separate the addict from
others and enables the healing process to continue.

There is guidance available for counselors and sponsors to provide this feedback during the client's Fifth
Step sharing. This can be found in pamphlets available
from AA or other Twelve Step Programs.

STEP SIX

*"Were entirely ready
to have God remove
all these defects of character."*

By this stage in the recovery process, the addict or alcoholic has generally had some period of sobriety. It
takes time to work through the previous steps, and many
become stuck along the way. What is significant is that,
even after all the hard work getting to this point, there
is still much more to do. It is during this step that addicts begin to grapple with unhealthy aspects of their
addictive personalities brought into recovery. A sorting of priorities occurs here, as they are asked to make
a list of the "defects of character" identified in Step Five
that they are ready to give up, and those that they are
not ready to "turn over." It is *conscious choice* that differentiates this process from their previous ways of
acting. As denial continues to dissolve, they begin to
learn that they alone are responsible for the ways they
feel and act, and the beliefs that continue to drive them.

This step requires addicts to look inside and ask, "Am
I ready to change?" From Dilts' logical levels model

of change, this requires work at the level of *identity*. For the therapist working with someone about to take Steps Six and Seven, it can be very helpful to complete an "ecological check" of *all* parts of the client. Where the Fourth and Fifth Steps uncovered private beliefs, cognitions and other "secrets" that bound the addict to the disease, the Sixth and Seventh Steps complete the process by focusing on eliminating many of these cognitive and behavioral ties to the addiction. Therapists will often find at this stage it is important to help the client work through change issues that involve *secondary gains*: behaviors and thoughts that hold special power over the individual, not for what they *are* but for what they *result in*. For example, if a person finds it difficult to "turn over" his fear of failure, it is important to discover what that fear accomplishes *for* the person. By using processes such as NLP's Six Step Reframing[16], the therapist can facilitate the addict's work in becoming "ready" to change.

Here again, Twelve Step members are asked to look outside themselves for help in making the changes. However, the "help" implied by these steps is much more complex than it appears. Through prayer and meditation, the addict communicates a willingness to make the identified changes in character and asks for guidance. During this process, he becomes aware that the response to these prayers will not be some instantaneous or magical reformation, but rather more concrete guidance. During this process, as he prays for help in overcoming fear, the addict learns that what must come first is acceptance of the help offered by other people in his life. He discovers that he must meet regularly with his Twelve Step sponsor or attend counseling sessions before the changes can begin. He discovers that the changes will come only with hard work, courage and persistence.

Step Six is preparatory to making change. It signals that the addict has become consciously aware of personality defects, those things about him that cause pain and prevent him from progressing and being productive in life. Drawing from the stage model of motivation, this represents work at the *determination* step. It sets the stage for the addict to initiate *action* towards a lifestyle change in Step Seven.

STEP SEVEN

"Humbly asked Him to remove our shortcomings."

For those with a belief in the traditional Judeo-Christian God, this step is part of a familiar process. Identifying one's sins, and admitting them to God, then asking for absolution is a sequence of events common to a number of religions. However, for those not steeped in such traditions, such an expectation may seem unrealistic or even preposterous. It is with many of these individuals that Gorski's concept of *rational spirituality*, where volition and consciousness are seen as important ingredients of recovery, can be very helpful. As Gorski puts it, his God says, "Choose and act, and you'll learn whether you did the right thing by the consequences" (p. 147). There is nothing mysterious or magical about removing defects of character. There is only courage and hard work. Courage, because such fundamental change is frightening: If I change who I am, then Who will I become? Hard work, because old patterns of behavior, our "comfortable habits" require persistent attention and effort to change.

Taking this step reaffirms Twelve Step members' commitment to continuing recovery. When they take this step, they are taking *action* to change. The age old adage, "God helps those who help themselves," applies here. It is important at this stage, however, to remember one of Maultsby's *facts*: we are all "fallible human beings."[17] There are some things the addict simply cannot change, and there are some things he may not yet be ready to change.

One of my favorite sayings popularized by the Twelve Step programs is the "Serenity Prayer." The short version asks that "God grant me the serenity to accept the things I cannot change, the courage to change the things I can, and the wisdom to know the difference." This is sage advice to the confused and overwhelmed addict who has begun to work on his internal resources. Cognitive restructuring of such scope as implied by Step Seven is understandably frightening. The ability to select the areas to focus on is greatly facilitated by appreciating that we are not perfect, any of us, and that the addict needs to accept those aspects of his being (his past behaviors and present limitations) that he cannot change.

It is at this step that many in the program find themselves turning to other resources such as therapy or counseling. The complexities of the addict's internal processes and the power of well-rehearsed patterns of behavior can be baffling. Therapists who specialize in helping people identify what needs to be changed and provide the specific techniques for accomplishing those changes are in an ideal position to support the addict at this stage of recovery.

STEP EIGHT

> *"Made a list of all persons*
> *we had harmed,*
> *and became willing*
> *to make amends to them all."*

Rephrasing this step using the stage model of motivation, addicts are asked to contemplate the nature and effects of their addictive behaviors, make a list of those who have suffered on their account, and then become determined to take appropriate action. During their progression into addiction to chemicals or other compulsive behaviors, addicts do tremendous damage to others in their lives. We find they have lied and cheated and stolen. They have regularly abused significant others emotionally and physically and have isolated themselves from normal social relationships. The memories of these past behaviors cause tremendous guilt and remorse in recovering individuals. Such feelings tend to significantly lower self-esteem and distort the person's self-image. The net result of such a twisted self concept is often poor motivation to change. "I'm not worth the effort," and "Why even bother; it's already too late," are common thoughts as the addict contemplates entering treatment or struggles with the decision to stay.

When the recovering addict arrives at the point where he is ready to face his past, his mistakes and failures, and the damage done to his relationships, this signals a tremendously powerful shift in a his internal resources. As with Step Six, the addict must operate here from the level of his *identity*. Taking this step also indicates that he is moving away from an external *locus of control* and working towards accepting responsibility for his role in what occurs to him in his life. At this stage, rather than continuing to blame others as they frequently did during their using period, addicts begin looking at the effects their own behavior has had on others. The focus of this step demonstrates a reorientation of the addict's process of relating with others and represents a developing ability to accept accountability for the role they have played in their relationships.

This sorting out of those wronged in preparation to ask for forgiveness has a flip side as well. One of the most common "character defects" we encounter is *resentment*[18]. A by-product of denial, the practicing addict or alcoholic was quick to point the finger at others who refused to enable or who "took advantage" of his condition. I don't mean to imply that the addict was never wronged along the way. Even in his disease, he is still a vulnerable human being. The point is, he needs to prevent those memories from effecting the quality of his sobriety. Thus, while making the list of those he has harmed, the addict is asked to also make a list of past transgressors. In preparing to ask for forgiveness, the addict also prepares to forgive, thus eliminating one of the "drivers" that have the potential to initiate a return to use.

STEP NINE

*"Made direct amends
to such people wherever possible,
except when to do so
would injure them or others."*

In reintegrating addicts back into the society from which they have alienated and isolated themselves, it is imperative that they come to terms with the inevitable guilt and shame and make appropriate restitution for the wrongs they have done. This step accomplishes both if done as suggested. It is not a simple apology the addict makes. It is admitting that under the duress of the addiction, the addict said and did things he would not have otherwise said or done. It is taking responsibility for both his actions and their consequences.

In a way, this is a more refined but dramatic version of Step Five. In Step Five, the addict only had to confess to God and another human being his past transgressions. In Step Eight he must take full responsibility for his past actions by making direct amends. Making restitution is a requirement of this *action* step. If the addict stole property, it needs to be returned or compensated for. Material things are often easier to repair than emotional transgressions. However, the act of admitting to those from his past that while he was drinking or drugging he caused them pain and hardship, that now he knows and understands his role in causing them pain, and that he is sorry can go a long way towards healing the past.

This can be a very uplifting step; however, as suggested, it needs to be taken with care. There are those to whom an amend would be considered an affront and those who would find old wounds opening that had already healed. There are situations where new relationships could be traumatized or strained by such admissions and are best left alone. The addict needs to evaluate whether or not his actions might "cause harm to them or others" and act accordingly.

The other major risk at this stage is the possibility that the addict will react strongly to the responses he gets from others. When taking this step, the addict may have to face rejection or anger or even rage. These emotions were often triggers in the past for the addict to use in order to cope with them. Now, finally sober, he must bear up under the brunt of accusations, face the pain and anger of others *without* resorting to past coping behaviors. Working closely with his counselor and keeping strong contact with his sponsor, who himself has "been through it" can be important to the addict who is taking Step Nine.

Each of the last six steps involved activities oriented towards making lifestyle change towards health and sobriety. The Twelve Step member was asked first to contemplate, then to become determined, and finally to act in a sequence emulating the second through fourth stages in the stage model of motivation. The following three steps represent the next stage in that model called *maintenance.* By regularly practicing each of these steps, recovering addicts keep themselves on a clean and sober track and reinforce spiritual, psychological, and social elements of recovery so hard won.

STEP TEN

> *"Continued to take personal inventory*
> *and when we were wrong*
> *promptly admitted it."*

The Twelve Step program is generally accepted as a *daily* program of recovery. For most people in recovery, there are certain things that must be done on a regular basis in order to stay clean and sober. Part of this daily routine is what is often referred to as "daily housecleaning." The Twelve Step recovery process suggests that participants constantly monitor and regularly review their progress. Step Ten ensures this is done.

Many people recovering in the Twelve Step programs develop a morning and evening ritual. Part of this ritual is to review each of the steps. They may begin their day by reaffirming the first three steps. These are sometimes shortened to "I can't, God can, I believe I'll let Him." The evening meditation will find them "going inside" to find if there are any fears, anger, or resentments left over from the day's activities. Journal writing and calling one's sponsor to discuss problems encountered during the day is a Fifth Step, while reading self-help literature and attending meetings provides support for continued change (Steps Six and Seven). Steps Eight and Nine can also be accomplished by a brief phone call or visit as soon as reasonable after the wrong has been identified, like, "I'm sorry I yelled at you today. It's an old habit I'm trying to change. I was actually only concerned about...", etc. The process is generally followed by a period of meditation or prayer (Step Eleven), while regular participation in the fellowship facilitates the Twelfth Step.

TENTH STEP RITUAL

The inventory in Step Ten is generally a review of the recent past, the day's experiences, thoughts, feelings and actions. While not as extensive an inventory as the Fourth Step, it does promote positive cognitive change. Many in the program, especially in early recovery, keep a daily journal. It is sometimes a pleasant surprise to look back over entries made only a few weeks earlier and see how much progress has been made. Writing in a journal can also help the addict organize his thoughts and stay on track; remember, many of these individuals have only recently begun to explore their inner selves, and it is easy to become distracted by irrelevant issues. These are often the result of parts of the addict that want to sabotage his recovery efforts because they haven't been fully integrated into the "new" person. By sharing the journal with his therapist, these problems can be uncovered and worked with during counseling sessions.

STEP ELEVEN

*"Sought through prayer and meditation
to improve our conscious contact
with God as we understood him,
praying only for knowledge
of His will for us and
the power to carry that out."*

As a person works through the steps, there are continual reminders of the need to develop trust in one's Higher Power. Often referred to as "HP", this "Power greater than ourselves" continues to evolve during the process of recovery through the Twelve Step programs. It is not at all unusual for the newcomer to refer to his Higher Power as the AA group, or even simply the words spoken during the meetings. As the individual continues to grow through the steps, his relationship with his HP changes. Using the name "God" to identify this source of spiritual guidance and inspiration becomes habitual for many in the program regardless of past or present religious beliefs.

The term "God" can be considered a shorthand for a *relationship* that continues to grow and develop between the recovering person and his HP. It is important to underscore the personal aspect of this relationship. AA facilitates this personalized relationship by highlighting here and in the Third Step the words "*as we understood him*." This "officially condones" individualized interpretations of God and demonstrates just how open minded the founders of AA were. Open mindedness is a keystone of the program, and it is built into the very fabric of its principles.

As therapists and counselors, we need to be sensitive to each client's personal interpretation of this entity. Interactions the client has with his HP can be utilized during the course of a therapy session. We can build upon the client's understanding of the communication, assist the client in interpreting the messages, or reinforce positive behavioral changes perceived by the client just as we would with any resource the client brings to the session. As discussed in Step Two, the therapist can also assist the client to identify and build solid communication with an internalized HP such as a meta part or "worthy advisor."

Built into every Twelve Step meeting, and recommended as part of members' daily rituals, is the process of prayer and meditation. Because this is often a new behavior for many, it takes practice. Newcomers frequently ask, "How do I know when my HP is talking to me?" As they listen to others describing their relationship with God, however, the newcomer begins to recognize the "messages" himself, and integrates them into his recovery processes. The ritual of meditation and prayer are also significant in that they represent new cognitive-behavioral strategies for such tasks as problem solving, dealing with upsetting emotions and events, and relaxation *in the absence of drugs, alcohol or other compulsive behaviors.*

Gorski's (1989) definition of God may be helpful for those struggling with this concept. He describes God as "the central value that provides order, meaning, and purpose to everything else we do" (p. 189). He suggests that if an atheist believes that science is the organizing principle in his life, then science can become that person's God. "If we organize our life around reason, our God is reason. If we organize it around getting drunk and throwing up, our GOD is booze" (p. 189). Continuing with dysfunctional patterns of behavior, then, an overeater's God is food, a gambler's God is the track, and a codependent's God is the addict who is controlling his life. What happens during the work involved in taking the Twelve Steps is that a person redefines his God towards a more constructive, helpful, and forgiving entity.

Step Eleven encourages recovering addicts to continue to work on their relationship with their HP. It suggests that staying clean and sober will be made easier by listening to the guidance they get and carrying out the instructions, completing the tasks, and working a program of recovery. It supports their search for meaning and purpose in life, for it is that sense of direction that strengthens an addict's resolve to stay clean and sober. Given meaning in life, the addict feels less worthless, and provided a purpose, less isolated. By practicing on a daily basis activities that enhance self-concept and encourage more positive interactions, he will continue to mold his life and grow and change in positive directions.

STEP TWELVE

"Having had a spiritual awakening
as the result of these steps,
we tried to carry the message
to alcoholics and to practice these
principles in all our affairs."

Appendix II of *Alcoholics Anonymous* talks about the "Spiritual Experience." While one of the founders of AA talked earlier about having had an abrupt spiritual experience, this section describes the more typical "personality changes" a person can expect after entering a Twelve Step program. It says that the transformation occurs slowly over time:

Quite often friends of the newcomer are aware of the difference long before he is himself. He finally realizes that he has undergone a profound alteration in his reaction to life; that such a change could hardly have been brought on by himself alone. What takes place in a few months could seldom have been accomplished by years of self discipline. With few exceptions our members find that they have tapped an unsuspected inner resource which they presently identify with their own conception of a Power greater than themselves (pp. 569-570).

The addict/alcoholic, after years of living in isolation within a private hell of his own making is required by the Twelfth Step to continue the resocialization process. One common saying in the fellowship is "If you want it, you have to give it away." The basic philosophical underpinnings of the Twelve Step programs has always been "one drunk talking to another." This forces the alcoholic to relate outside of himself. It takes away the tendency towards self-centeredness and fosters healthy interactions. And it gives the recovering addict a "higher purpose" in life, another avenue for making amends and rectifying his past.

Alcoholics, addicts, gamblers, overeaters, adult children of alcoholics, co-dependents and members of other Twelve Step programs get together to "share their experience, strength and hope." As one person in recovery speaks to others, there is an opportunity for those listening to learn from his experiences, from his mistakes and successes, to identify with someone outside of themselves. To hear the speaker talk about his own progress in recovery gives the newcomer hope where before was only despair. And when he finds he can also give this hope to others, he begins to feel OK about himself. It gives life new meaning and purpose around which he can organize himself and continue to grow more productive. It gives him an important reason to continue to live clean and sober.

This means that the recovering addict must practice the principles of all the Twelve Steps on a regular basis. He needs to both "talk the talk and walk the walk" to be able to carry the message to others. As we have discussed in previous sections, recovery is an ongoing process. That means that the person continues to grow, to evolve. This transformation can be slow and subtle, or it can be dramatic. It is an energy that attracts others; there is no need to proselytize in AA; in fact, it bills itself as a "program of attraction". It does this by its recovering members *modeling* healthy recovery and being open and willing to share what they have with others more needy.

TAKING THE FIRST THREE STEPS

Many in the fellowship consider the first three steps to be the most important. Each step is ingeniously set up to assist the addict in a progressively higher level of change. By "practicing" at first one level, and then the next, the individual has an opportunity to begin to reorganize himself. The reorganization is not haphazard. It is progressive in a specific direction: towards a fundamental change in personal identity.

The shift does not take place quickly. In fact, many in the fellowship tell stories of taking months and years to take the first three steps. However, generally speaking, once the participants have taken these steps, it is likely they will continue through the remainder of the Twelve Steps, and, as noted previously, those who stay in the program for more than one year are statistically more likely to remain sober the following year.

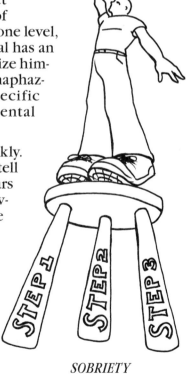

SOBRIETY

NINETY MEETINGS IN NINETY DAYS

One of the pieces of wisdom coming out of the AA movement is the "requirement" that newcomers and those just being released from treatment attend 90 meetings during the next 90 days. There is a good reason for this. Have you ever been to a motivational lecture and, as you were leaving, found yourself saying, "I'm pumped. I *will* do all those things I've been promising myself I'd do all these years." Of course, the next day finds you half asleep on the couch with National Geo, a bottle of coke, and the ninth round of the US Open on the tube. Reality sets in. Those great feelings you got at the seminar or meeting the night before simply don't last.

AA members are aware of this tendency. It takes real dedication to make the lifestyle changes required by the Twelve Step programs. This kind of dedication takes practice. The motivation to practice must be constantly stoked, and the best stoke in the world is to sit in a room with others in recovery and share their experience, strength and hope. In three months, *maybe* the newcomer will have enough practice to keep it up during periods between the meetings.

There's another reason for "90 in 90." Twelve step programs function both as a product of the inherent *therapy* of the 12 steps and as a product of the *fellowship* of the program. By requiring close interaction with fellow AAers during these meetings, even the most shy and withdrawn individuals can be drawn out and "included" in the group processes. This fosters the interdependence of group members, encourages participation, and reinforces the bonding between members in support of their sobriety.

AA IS NOT FOR EVERYBODY

While the Twelve Step self-help groups continue to lead the way as the most popular form of recovery from chemical addiction and compulsive mood altering activities, they are not without their critics. Fingarette (1988) makes a very compelling argument against AA's support of the classic disease concept of alcoholism. He claims that most problem drinkers in the United States not only do not see themselves as alcoholics, but also would not be diagnosed as alcoholics, because they would not fit enough of the criteria for such a diagnosis. Many newcomers to the meetings are turned off by the emphasis on the spiritual aspects of the program, regardless of how "softly" it is peddled. Still others do not see addiction as a "life-long" disease, believing that, once stability is regained and abstention is maintained, there is no longer a need to work a daily program of recovery. It is likely because of these problems that several alternative groups now offer self-help for those who do not fit in with the Twelve Step programs.

RATIONAL RECOVERY

Rational Recovery was founded in 1986 by Jack Trimpey who had tried the Twelve Step programs but found them lacking. He has written an alternative to AA's "Big Book", called *Rational Recovery from Alcoholism: The Small Book* (Trimpey, 1989) which presents an approach to recovery based on Rational-Emotive Therapy (RET), one of the most popular forms of cognitive-behavioral therapy. He writes, "A good questioning technique is 'So what stops you from planning to never drink (use) again?' Here you may encounter major resistance accompanied by acute anxiety, for the client's addictive voice, the Beast of RR, will intrude with many reasons why one *must* not decide now to never drink again" (p. 228).

A key element in the rational mode of recovery is The Big Plan, i.e., a commitment or desire to never use or drink again. Never (Jack Trimpey, 1989, p. 228).

The "Rational Recovery Ideas" listed below reflect a philosophically different approach to the addiction and recovery than AA's Twelve Steps. Trimpey (1989) describes Rational Recovery as the "counterpoint" to AA and suggests that the Twelve Step programs foster dependence rather than freedom from dependence. The following eleven "Rational Ideas for Recovery" printed in italics below are from Trimpey's (1989) "small book" (pp. 273-274).

1. *I admit that I have become chemically dependent, and the consequences of that dependency are unacceptable.* Note the similarity between this rational cognitive statement and Step One of AA. The choice of the term "chemically dependent" rather than "powerless over alcohol" is an indication of a different focus that becomes clear as these "ideas" are repeated.

2. *I accept that, in order to get better, I will have to refrain from any use of alcohol, because any use will very likely lead to more, and a return to my previous addiction.* In the Twelve Step programs, abstention is not even addressed in the Twelve Steps, but rather in the third Tradition: "The only requirement for A.A. membership is a desire to stop drinking." However, underlying the AA program is the medical model which clearly mandates abstention as a requirement for recovery.

3. *I accept that I will likely benefit from outside help in accomplishing this, because I have been unsuccessful in previous attempts to resist my desire to drink.* Here, rather than turning to a "higher power," the participant in RR is encouraged to turn to "outside help." While AA does not discourage its members from seeking help from physicians, psychologists, counselors and others, the primary curative process is the spiritual transformation discussed earlier.

4. *Although I may have serious personal problems, I still have the capacity to learn about myself, new ideas, and how to achieve a durable and meaningful sobriety.* At the core of cognitive-behavioral therapies is the idea that our clients have this "capacity to learn."

5. *The idea that I need something greater than myself upon which to rely is only another dependency idea, and dependency is my original problem.* Here, RR makes its greatest break with the principles of AA.

This fundamental difference is actually what makes RR so appealing to many of its participants, most of whom tried AA first, but were unable or unwilling to "Turn it over," and "Let go and let God."

6. *I surrender all ideas of perfection, for myself and others, and my first goal is to learn to accept myself as I am, a fallible, yet very worthwhile, human being.* This is an interesting play on words. In AA, "surrender" implies turning one's will and life over "to the care of God *as we understood Him.*" Here it means giving up irrational ideas and ideals.

7. *I place a high value on the principles of rationality, learning, objectivity, self-forgiveness, and on my own self-interest.* This is a good example of a rational statement that could be used in place of derogatory self statements.

8. *I recognize the desperate need of others for a rational recovery plan, so I may take these ideas to them, as a way of creating a larger society of sober, rational people.* This is RR's version of the Twelfth Step, where we are instructed to "carry this message" to others who suffer. This has the same effect as the process in AA, namely, it helps the addict to focus outward rather than continue the social isolation that has helped support the addiction.

9. *Recognizing that there is much more to life than a constant struggle to remain sober, and having gained a reasonable expectation that I can live a meaningful life without alcohol or drugs, I will gradually separate myself from my RR group — with the understanding that I may return at any time.* Here again is a fundamental break with the principles of AA. RR attempts to foster *independence* from the group, while AA sees the fellowship as one of the primary curative factors of the program.

10. *I accept that there are no perfect solutions to life's problems and that uncertainty is the spice of life, so therefore I am willing to take risks to achieve my own self-defined goals.* This idea echoes numbers 4, 6, and

7 above where the individual is encouraged to continue to grow and learn more about him or herself. Life is full of opportunities to test our limits and expand ourselves, but this kind of learning is fraught with risks. This statement reframes these risks as "the spice of life."

11. *Now certain of my inherent worth, I can take the risks of loving, for loving is far better than being loved.* This rational statement addresses one of the common irrational beliefs that our clients bring to therapy: To feel worthy, I must be loved. Especially true of the population of chemically dependent clients, this rational statement shifts the responsibility for action back to the client.

SECULAR ORGANIZATIONS FOR SOBRIETY

S.O.S. Sobriety was developed by James Christopher for many of the same reasons Jack Trimpey developed his Rational Recovery program. Recognized as a viable alternative to AA for those needing self-help recovery, S.O.S. groups have begun to increase in popularity. Similar to Rational Recovery in size, S.O.S. groups offer participants an opportunity to develop a program of recovery without reliance on what some see as A.A.'s "religiosity."

I present these alternatives to AA here, simply because they are viable alternatives for involving our clients in self-help recovery activities that appear to work. Although not common, I have had opportunities to suggest to my own clients that they might find in RR or S.O.S. what they were unable to get from AA. One nice thing about RR is how well it supports and teaches many of the patterns of rational thinking used in CBT during the therapy sessions. The only problem with both RR and S.O.S. is that they remain small, and therefore the meetings are less frequent and less well attended than most Twelve Step meetings. But, of course, this in itself is appealing to some clients.

NOTES FOR CHAPTER 4

1. These statistics come from the General Services Office of Alcoholics Anonymous (1988).

2. Besides the "Big Book" *Alcoholics Anonymous*, AA Publications puts out a number of pamphlets, booklets and the monthly periodical "The A.A. Grapevine." Other Twelve Step organizations (Narcotics Anonymous, Gamblers Anonymous, etc.) also produce books, booklets and other information. Many of these are available at cost at your local Fellowship (see your phone book), and at most Twelve Step meetings.

3. The Oxford Groups contribution to AA will be discussed in the section "How It Works".

4. A distinction that is important to this discussion needs to be clarified here. There is a significant difference between *treatment* and *recovery*. One writer, Eric Griffin-Shelley (1990), writes, "Recovery differs from treatment in that it is the ongoing, lifelong process of change that an individual undertakes to maintain abstinence" (p. 4). He goes on to describe how most AA members describe themselves as *recovering* rather than *recovered* alcoholics, stating, "This reflects their acceptance of alcoholism as a chronic disease that can only be arrested, never cured" (p. 4). This statement, of course, reflects the primary premise of the American Disease model of addiction.

5. All quotes in this section attributed to the "Big Book" come from *Alcoholics Anonymous* (3rd Ed., 1976).

6. A complete description of the role of the Oxford Group on the formation of AA, and a thorough documentation of AA's origins is contained in a wonderfully readable book, *Getting Better, Inside Alcoholics Anonymous*, by Nan Robertson (1988).

7. There are a number of outstanding books and pamphlets that discuss the Twelve Steps. One that I highly recommend is Gorski's (1989) *Understanding the Twelve Steps: A Guide for Counselors, Therapists, and Recovering People*. There are also other resources available. AA World Services produces the *Twelve Steps and Twelve Traditions* which can be obtained at cost from almost every Twelve Step program in your area. I also strongly recommend the reading of *Alco-*

holics Anonymous, the "Big Book," chapters 5, 6, and 7 and/ or chapters 4 and 5 in *Narcotics Anonymous*. Finally, Hazelden produces a tremendous number of booklets, workbooks, and pamphlets on various aspects of the Twelve Steps. See "Resources" at Appendix 1.

8. The First Step of each of the Twelve Step programs has been modified to reflect the nature of the problem being addressed.

9. Lewis and Pucelik, 1982.

10. The paradox of *surrender* will be covered in the section on Step Three.

11. Bateson (1972) writes, "In sum I shall argue that the 'sobriety' of the alcoholic is characterized by an unusually disastrous variant of the Cartesian dualism, the division between Mind and Matter, or, in this case, between conscious will, or 'self,' and the remainder of the personality. Bill W.'s stroke of genius was to break up with the first 'step' the structuring of this dualism" (p. 313).

12. Seen within the context of the era in which this program was developed, this presupposition makes a great deal of sense. At that time, alcoholics who had progressed to the point of physical deterioration were regularly locked up in mental wards and other institutions for the insane. It was considered a psychiatric problem with little hope for recovery.

13. Gorski (1989) writes, "...the first HP for the majority of recovering people is the power of their recovery group. It's the power of the group conscience, the collective energy and help available from that group" (p. 96).

14. The serenity prayer embodies the essence of the third step:

God, grant me the serenity
to accept the things I cannot change,
the courage to change the things I can,
and the wisdom to know the difference.

15. Nan Robertson (1988) describes in great detail the various meetings and experiences both Bill W. and Bob S. had with the Oxford Groups and with various influential members of the organization.

16. Bandler and Grinder's (1982) model for addressing this issue has the client separate the behavior from its *positive* *intention*, then replace it with alternative behaviors which will still fulfill the positive intention.

17. The "fallible human being" (FHB) is a repeating theme in many of Maultsby's works. One of the best descriptions occurs in his tape series "Including Therapeutic Self-Help in Counseling and Psychotherapy; Theory and Practice of Group Rational Behavior Therapy", Rational Behavior Therapy Center, 1982. At one point, Maultsby exclaims, "We are all fallible Human Beings. We never do everything 100% perfectly except die, and we can't even do that perfectly with modern medicine anymore!"

18. Gorski (1989) has a particularly good cognitive-behavioral description of resentment. He writes, "Resentment comes from the word 'resent.' 'Re' means to do over again. 'Sent' or 'send' means to resend; to send the same message to my brain over and over again. That's a resentment" (p. 164). You can see the significant impact this has on a person struggling to stay emotionally calm and stable while making the lifestyle changes required by the recovery process.

5

IRRATIONAL THOUGHT

Cognitive Therapy

is based on the observation

that dysfunctional automatic thoughts

that are exaggerated, distorted, mistaken,

or unrealistic in other ways play a

major role in psychopathology

(Freeman, et. al., 1990, p. 4).

Starting with this chapter and continuing in those that follow, I will present various techniques from NLP and CBT that have direct applications to substance abuse and compulsive disorders counseling. In keeping with the first section of the book, I have drawn analogies and made comparisons between the two technologies where applicable. For the most part, what you will find presented are general overviews of each technique. I strongly urge interested readers to obtain the original works of the authors and researchers cited herein for more complete and detailed explanations of the techniques.

As with any treatment methodology, there needs to be a marriage between technique, client, and therapist. As a clinician, you may find some of these techniques more comfortable to use than others. Experience shows that some clients respond better to certain approaches than others. In Chapter 3 the Stage Model of Motivation demonstrated that certain techniques will be more appropriate at specific stages of the client's problem than others. Throughout the process, regardless of the counselor, client, or technique involved, there are certain key factors that make for successful therapy. It is to these that we will first turn our attention.

BEGINNING THE WORK

Before starting, let me share with you some personal thoughts about *therapy*. Therapy is not something that a counselor *does* to a client, and it is not simply the application of some technique or another. The changes that occur as a result of therapeutic interventions are the product of the *interaction* between the client and the *therapeutic environment*. This environment includes the therapist, the office, the group or family if involved, and myriad other factors. The primary responsibility of the therapist or counselor is to orchestrate the environment to create optimal conditions which will facilitate therapeutic change within the client.

Initially, such orchestration requires attention to two major areas. The first is the development of a good therapeutic relationship. Critical to this relationship is the therapist's ability to gain and maintain rapport with the client. The second is the ability to develop an appropriate therapeutic outcome. The experienced therapist will recognize that both of these are *processes*; that is, they are ongoing aspects of the interaction between the therapist and the client. As the therapist adjusts the work then readjusts again in response to the client's feedback and to maintain rapport, the end state evolves, becoming both a product and an affecter of the session itself.

RAPPORT

Persuasive and directive approaches to therapy such as those employed in CBT and NLP require the client to

have a great deal of trust and confidence in the therapist[1]. Regardless of the approach or techniques you may
utilize during a session, maintaining rap-
port is extremely important to the *...being right is far less*
therapeutic process. In fact, the success *therapeutic and*
of some s can depend entirely on the *important than being*
client's trust and confidence in the thera- *effectively persuasive...*
pist. The process of gaining (Ellis, et. al.,
rapport – from matching the client's 1988, p. 55).
predicates (sensory words) to more subtle
mirroring of unconscious behaviors – is more than adequately covered in many of the NLP volumes[2]. Don't
misunderstand me here. Rapport does *not* preclude
therapeutic confrontation. Quite the contrary, confrontation is often extremely useful to help the client begin
to open the door to alternative ways of thinking. The
therapist must simply be sensitive to the client's feedback to determine how hard and how far to push.

While gaining rapport may be the single most important part in developing a therapeutic relationship,
it can be one of the most difficult processes to teach
new therapists and counselors. One of the most dramatically useful tools created by the originators of
NLP applies directly to the process of gaining and
maintaining rapport. NLP teaches the counselor how
to *map the client's representational systems*. During this process you systematically identify the
portions of sensory experience the client uses to
perceive and *understand* the world using both verbal and nonverbal cues. This information is then
utilized during the therapy session to enhance concise and smooth communication and identify deficits
and boundaries to the client's model that may hinder
therapeutic change[3].

Throughout the therapeutic interaction, the therapist
gauges the client's responses, pushing as hard and as
fast as the client is able to respond, and backing off
when rapport is lost. One useful therapeutic approach from CBT that facilitates rapport is described
by Freeman, et. al. (1990). Using this approach, called
guided discovery, the therapist asks questions de-

signed to guide the client to an understanding of the problem, identify possible solutions, and develop a working plan for dealing with specifics of implementation. This cognitive therapeutic approach is the result of what Freeman calls "collaborative empiricism", wherein the counselor works with clients to help them "...recognize cognitions and other factors that cause problems..., to test the validity of the thoughts, beliefs, and assumptions that prove important, and to make the needed changes in both cognition and behavior" (p. 9). As you read through the descriptions and case examples of the works cited on these pages, whether NLP, RBT, RET or other CBT approaches, you will find this process consistently being utilized.

As previously discussed, rapport goes beyond the relationship between client and counselor. There are a number of other methods of gaining rapport that can be especially effective with the addicted client. The following are just a few examples the clinician may want to consider.

The office environment itself can be important to the process of gaining rapport. An attentive counselor can gain quick inroads in the work by incorporating the client's responses to certain environmental cues into the therapy. You might consider, for example, having available in plain view a copy of *Alcoholics Anonymous*, *Twenty-Four Hours A Day* or other Twelve Step literature. These books can elicit a strong response from clients who have been exposed to the Twelve Step programs. For many, they will have special meaning, and the astute practitioner will be able to utilize this meaning during the course of treatment.

For example, if the client exhibits a very positive response to the sight of *The Big Book*, the therapist can *anchor* this response (pair a neutral stimulus to the response) for later use in developing resources with the client. If, however, the client has an aversive reaction to such materials, the therapist can quickly gain rapport by discussing the client's perceived limitations of these programs (*pacing*) while paving the way to other cognitive-behavioral approaches to treatment (*leading*)[4].

THERAPEUTIC OUTCOME

Identifying the appropriate goal for therapy is the other critical process in creating an effective therapeutic environment. I particularly like the metaphor Cameron-Bandler, et. al. (1985a) use to underscore the importance of selecting a therapeutic outcome. Without an explicit outcome to guide the process, they say, "It would be like asking a stranger whether you should turn right or left at the next corner without having first decided where you want to go" (p. 198).

There are several areas to consider when identifying therapeutic goals with a client. The NLP counselor will often ask the client to describe a *well-formed outcome*. This outcome must satisfy five specific criteria in order to be considered well-formed:

1. **POSITIVE**. The outcome must be stated in *positive terms*. There is a big difference between a client saying "I don't want to argue with my spouse any more," and "I want to learn better communication skills."[5]

2. **OBSERVABLE**. There must be some way for the person to evaluate his or her progress towards the goal using normal sensory channels. "I want to learn how to get more attention from him," is not as easily observed as "I want to learn how to get more hugs from him."

3. **CLIENT-CONTROLLED**. The behaviors that will produce the outcome must be initiated and maintained by the client, rather than by some outside agency or person. In the example above, notice that the client says, "I want to learn how to get more hugs," rather than, "I want *him* to give me more hugs."

4. ECOLOGICALLY SOUND. A well-formed outcome preserves the positive aspects of the client's present state. This is a tricky one for substance abuse counselors. A goal of "sobriety", for example, requires considerable change in the client's lifestyle, all of which will not be easy or comfortable. However, when we place it on the scale against the client's current state and weigh such things as health, happiness, marriage, etc., it is easy to see the positive gains outweigh short-term discomforts.

5. REALISTIC. Finally, the goal must conform to fit realistically with the rest of the client's life. As a goal, "I want to be free from obligations at home," could result in a divorce which may not necessarily be in the best interests of the client. A more well-formed goal would be, "I want to learn how to live more comfortably at home."

As with all aspects of the therapeutic relationship, the client needs to be actively involved in this process. By facilitating an open and trusting relationship, the counselor fosters a sense of mutual self-respect and dignity with the client. There will be times to confront, to push, and to challenge the client. Encouraging the client to participate in the decisions regarding his or her treatment goals may result in a lot less resistance during these difficult times.

When developing appropriate goals with your clients, it can also be important to take into consideration the type of referral you are working with. A court-mandated client may bring a different set of expectations and motivation to therapy than one who has entered treatment on his or her own. Determining the stage of motivation of your client as discussed in Chapter Three and working it into the goals you establish will make your work go more smoothly in the long run. As noted by Ellis, et. al. (1988), failure to achieve therapeutic goals can result in the client forming negative associations to the therapeutic process. By setting realistic goals that are well-formed and match the level of motivation of the client, the successful therapeutic relationship is greatly enhanced.

COGNITIVE DISTORTIONS

Each school of thought in the CBT arena use various cognitive disputational techniques to help clients shift their faulty thinking towards more healthy and holistic ways of operating. Most of these techniques require an active-directive style of intervention. Whenever we intervene with these techniques, the need to maintain rapport becomes even more important. I vividly recall during the early years while learning the Meta Model techniques, a number of us in John Grinder's linguistics class at UCSC became adept at recognizing and challenging these speech patterns in others. In fact, we soon became known as "Meta Monsters", because we were unwilling to let absolutely any infraction pass by unchallenged! It was during that time that some of us learned — painfully at times — the importance of rapport.

Cognitive distortions are ways of thinking which limit client's choices about how to feel and act. They are generally indicative of areas the therapist can work with the client to produce the most rapid changes. Clients are usually unconscious of their automatic thoughts, and it is during therapeutic sessions that training in thought recognition and restructuring is accomplished. As the therapist points out specific dysfunctional thoughts and demonstrates the negative effects they have on the client's life, through repetition and practice, the client begins to internalize the process.

Simply recognizing dysfunctional thoughts, however, does not necessarily change them. In fact, even after being shown the negative consequences of a specific thought, some of our clients will tenaciously hold on to the thought and continue to believe in its validity unless there is further intervention. This involves the process of *cognitive disputation* in which the therapist asks the client specific types of questions designed to help uncover the inconsistencies, illogic, or unrealistic aspects of such thinking. Once the client is able to accept such thoughts as irrational or nonproductive, the therapist can

assist him or her to develop a healthier, more constructive set of thoughts with which to replace them.

THE NLP META MODEL

Bandler and Grinder's original work on the structure
of therapeutic change pivoted on their linguistic representation of the process. As these authors put it, "The
Meta Model is ... the *foundation* of everything we do."[6]
Basically, the Meta Model is used as a means for identifying irrational beliefs or cognitive distortions in clients
perceptions of themselves and the world, then disputing these distortions to help expand their options for
feeling and behaving. A major difference between their
work and the work of Ellis in RET, for example, is that a
Meta Model challenge is generated by the *structure* of
the client's language, rather than the *content* of his
message. Where RET will challenge the irrational beliefs in the client's statements, the NLP therapist will
challenge the structure of the linguistic pattern that
supports such a belief.

As described by Bandler & Grinder (1979b) and Lewis
& Pucelik (1982) among others, the Meta Model violations result from the *universal human modeling
processes*: generalization, deletion, and distortion. It
is through these processes that we cope with the complex profusion of input in our lives (from the cellular
level to the cognitive level.) They provide both the
means by which we can make sense of our world and
the limits we set on what we experience. When these
limits become so restrictive that we experience emotional pain or blocked growth, they need to be
challenged. The easiest way to study these distortions
is through the client's language, so this is where we
will start.

The model as presented in my first book (Lewis &
Pucelik, 1982) includes eight major linguistic distinctions. What follows is a brief description of each pattern
with the appropriate disputational response. Appendix

1 includes an abbreviated version of the same model organized around the disputational questions.

■ REFERENTIAL INDEX:

In a sentence, this is the person or thing doing or receiving the action of the verb. A *deleted referential index* usually indicates that the speaker is ignoring the agent or actor. As long as the deleted referential index remains unknown or unidentified, a client may experience a sense of loss of control or feelings of helplessness or hopelessness. For example, a client who says, "I feel neglected," can be helped to overcome feelings of helplessness if the counselor asks "Who is neglecting you?" This will refocus the client on the missing referent. Once it is identified, the client can begin to work towards understanding his or her part in the process of relating with that individual and re-establish a healthier and more realistic sense of participation and control within the relationship.

An *unspecified referential index* is where the client leaves out specifically who or what he is talking about. This Meta Model violation is often used as a form of denial or rationalization by clients in recovery. The counselor can challenge a statement like, "It won't make anything better" by asking, "What specifically won't make anything better?" The client's response can then be examined for validity.

UNSPECIFIED REFERENTIAL INDEX

Generalized referential index indicates that the client has extrapolated from one or a few experiences to an assumption about all cases. When a client says, "Therapists are all fruitcakes," you can help to open them up to alternative possibilities by asking, "What therapist did you think was a fruitcake."

Finally, *reversed referential index* is a case where the client indicates a sense of impotence or helplessness as the passive "victim" of the verb in a sentence. We often find this to be a reflection of a *projection* on the part of the client as in, "She treats me unfairly." This possibility can be explored by requesting the client to reverse the referents: "Tell me what you experience when you say, '*I* treat *her* unfairly.'" Popularized some time ago by the Gestalt therapist Fritz Perls[7], this form of challenge can be very powerful.

■ NOMINALIZATIONS:

Linguistically, this is the "nounifying" of verbs. Cognitively, it changes our perceptions of ongoing processes into static unchanging things. Clients in recovery often have tremendous difficulties with their *relationships*. A client may say, "My relationship with John is holding me back and threatening my recovery." Relationships, however, are not *things* but rather are ongoing *processes*. The client who uses this nominalized form of the verb *relating* effectively removes him or herself from the process. This fosters a sense of helplessness and loss of control. By helping clients to *denominalize* their distorted nouns back into action verbs, the therapist helps to guide them towards greater self efficacy. One appropriate response to the above utterance would be, "And just how is the way you and your boyfriend *are relating* holding you back?"

NOMINALIZATION

■ UNSPECIFIED VERBS:

These verbs foster unclear communication and promote confusion in the client's life. The more specific we are, both in our communication with others and in our own self-talk, the more effective and efficient we can be. The client who says, "He needs to show me he cares," has given us no indication of *what* he needs to do to demonstrate "care". The client may herself have no clear understanding of what she means until we ask her, "*How* would you like him to show you he cares." This challenge opens the door to clear and effective communication and models to the client appropriate cognitive methods for getting "unstuck".

■ MODAL OPERATORS:

These are a set of "auxiliary verbs" which include among others, *can*, *might*, *must*, *should*. There are two distinctions in this category that can prove fruitful if caught and challenged by the therapist.

Modal operators of necessity, are best exemplified by the words *should* and *must*. Challenging these words can help clients uncover unconscious "catastrophic expectations" that influence their behaviors. When a client says, "I shouldn't talk about what happened," the therapist asks, "What would happen if you did," enabling the client to bring into conscious awareness his or her fears. These can be further explored to determine if they are realistic or probable.[8]

Modal operators of possibility are evidence by words like *can* and *can't*. An utterance including the word *can't*, for example, demonstrates an absolute boundary to the client's beliefs about his or her capabilities. Again, challenging them can uncover potentially unrealistic or limiting beliefs that may be blocking growth and health. When a client says, "I can't tell them how I feel," the therapist responds with "What stops you?" This may open the door to exploration of self-imposed limits that are counterproductive to the client's life.

MODAL OPERATOR OF POSSIBILITY

■ UNIVERSAL QUANTIFIERS:

This linguistic distinction is similar to generalized referential index in that the client is making gross generalizations about life based on limited experiences. Cognitively disputing this Meta Model violation provides the opportunity to explore limits to the client's model of the world. Listen for words like *never*, *all*, or *every*, as in "Everybody drinks that much." The challenge points out counter examples, like, "Even your wife?" or "Name a few people you know who *don't* drink that much."

■ MIND READING:

The surreptitious presuppositions our clients make about the internal thoughts and emotions of others is a common distortion that needs to be challenged. When the client says, "She hates me for what I've done," it can be important to help the client learn that may not be true. If left undisputed, the client will continue to operate as if it is true, systematically defeating any attempts he or she might make to rectify the problem. By simply asking, "How do you know what she feels about you?" the therapist can help open the client's ability to perceive evidence to the contrary where it exists.

There is another intriguing cognitive of this pattern presented by DeRubeis and Beck (1988). Called the *downward arrow* technique, the therapist asks a series of questions where each answer from the client brings another question. In this case, the therapist would ask, "What would it mean *if it were true* that she hates you for what you've done?" The goal here is to help the client uncover a deeper personalized meaning for such an assumption about another's thoughts or feelings. This will often take the form of a belief about the client's self or *identity*.

MINDREADING

■ CAUSE AND EFFECT:

Another distortion of reality, this is where the client assumes that some action or statement causes another person to feel some emotion. This is a double-edged blade, however. The client may believe his actions cause others to have emotions; or he may believe that the words and actions of others cause him to have emotions. Either way, the client's choices about how to respond are severely limited by this belief. "She makes me want to get loaded," needs to be challenged with, "What does she do that you choose to become so upset about?"

■ LOST PERFORMATIVE:

Everyone has some internal standard by which they judge things as good or bad, helpful or harmful, etc. Sometimes,

LOST PERFORMATIVE

however, we find ourselves being unconsciously controlled by internalized standards that we simply don't agree with or find ourselves parroting standards that don't fit us. In these cases, the therapist can assist the client in regaining a more congruent perspective by challenging the client to either own the evaluation, belief or judgment or give it up. When a client says, "What I say and do really doesn't matter," the therapist can ask "Doesn't matter *to whom?*"

As the above examples demonstrate, the structure of the client's language is both revealing and functional. By systematically challenging the generalizations, deletions, and distortions presented as our clients talk about their problems, the therapist can significantly impact the health of the client's model of the world and assist in the cognitive transformations that are the hallmark of therapeutic change.

COGNITIVE ERRORS

One major goal of cognitive-based therapies is to teach clients that there are certain types of "thinking errors" associated with emotional distress. Beck originally identified six major cognitive errors used by cognitive therapists to aid in the teaching and challenging of these patterns of thinking[9]. An expanded set of common cognitive distortions are presented below[10]. Based on Beck's original work, these refer to a person's underlying assumptions about himself and his environment. You will notice that, like the Meta Model violations, they also stem from one or a combination of the "universal human modeling processes" of *generalization*, *deletion*, and *distortion*. Each of these cognitive distortions can result in behaviors — thoughts or beliefs, feelings, and actions — that demonstrate limits to the client's model of the world.

■ DICHOTOMOUS THINKING:

This is the "black or white thinking" often observed in alcoholics and addicts. From this absolutistic point of view, there is no "in between"; anything other than perfection is failure. A simple slip becomes the reason for a binge, because "I already failed anyway."

■ OVERGENERALIZATION:

Similar to Meta Model violation labeled "universal quantifier," this distinction results in the client's taking one experience and using it to generalize about all of life. Evidence of this pattern can be found in a client who shrugs in despair at the tasks of recovery, lamenting, "I've never succeeded at anything else. Why should I think I'll make it through this program?"

■ SELECTIVE ABSTRACTION:

This occurs when the client selectively highlights only one aspect of a situation or event to the exclusion of others. For example, my daughter comes home with a report card with one "D" and the rest "A's", but her focus is on the "D" exclusively. We also see this in the tendency for alcoholics rationalize continued abusive drinking by "comparing out". As discussed in Chapter 3, this is where they will find one "symptom" of alco-

SELECTIVE ABSTRACTION

holism they *don't* have and use that to "prove" they are not alcoholic.

■ DISQUALIFYING THE POSITIVE:

Anything that might shift attention away from a negativistic frame of mind is discounted by the client. The alcoholic in early recovery, for example, may be feeling deprived because he wants to drink at a party "like everyone else". When a friend notices he is abstaining and compliments his recovery efforts, rather than receiving the compliment and feeling good about himself, he shrugs it off with, "It's easy for *him* to say; he can *drink*."

■ MIND READING:

When our clients make assumptions about what others are thinking and feeling without any evidence, they are mind reading. Assuming the friend who complemented him for not drinking at the party last night was feeling sorry for him would be a good example. We also discussed the Meta Model violation of the same name.

■ FORTUNE-TELLING:

This is the basis for the old "self-fulfilling prophesy" where negative fantasies about the future come about because the client believes they will. The recovering gambler who believes his wife will leave him despite his solid recovery efforts will likely *act* in ways that make it uncomfortable for her to stay.

■ CATASTROPHIZING:

It is not uncommon to find our clients blowing out of proportion negative events in their lives. A newly sober client remembers being shy in social situations where alcohol wasn't served. Focusing on how awkward she always felt leads to believing that she will make an absolute fool of herself at her first sober party. She may become so distraught from this belief that she will refuse to attend the party or may use the belief as the excuse to "just have a few."

CATASTROPHIZING

■ MINIMIZATION:

This is different from the minimization we often encounter from abusers still in denial. This distortion occurs when positive events or experiences are "back tabled" because there are other more significant *problems*. "Sure, I didn't use today, but my life is still a *wreck*."

■ EMOTIONAL REASONING:

When clients make judgments about reality based on emotions rather than rational evaluations, they are using emotional reasoning. This occurs when, for example, a client believes he *is* helpless simply because he *feels* helpless.

■ "SHOULD" STATEMENTS:

These automatic thoughts motivate or provide control over the client's behavior in a negative way. What Ellis calls "musterbation" occurs when the client feels obligated or compelled to do (or *not* do) things based on these irrational thoughts. Also a Meta Model violation, this pattern was discussed as a "modal operator of necessity."

■ LABELING:

Hanging a name on yourself or others rather than describing behaviors is called labeling. "I made a foolish mistake," becomes "I am a fool." This is similar to the Meta Model violation "nominalization", where a process is changed to a static thing. One aspect of such transformations is that they can become reasons for not changing at all. It is easy to imagine changing our foolish behaviors, but how does one go about changing a fool? We will explore similar patterns in Chapter 7 when we deal with identity issues.

■ PERSONALIZATION:

A client who is taking responsibility for events outside his control is demonstrating this cognitive error. A good example would be the client who assumes he made his wife angry when she walked in angry over something that actually happened to her at work. This is the same pattern as the Meta Model violation "cause and effect."

The methods for disputing these cognitive errors vary. In the section that follows, I will outline effective approaches from RET and RBT. You will notice, however, unlike the Meta Model, the disputation of cognitive error shifts our attention away from the *structure* of the language itself and more towards the *content* or meaning behind the client's verbiage.

PERSONALIZATION

RET DISPUTATIONAL TECHNIQUES

When encountering statements made by a client that evidence irrational thinking, the RET therapist will generally utilize techniques to help the client evaluate rationally the statements. This process enables the client not only to determine the validity of such beliefs but also the potential benefits of changing them or letting them go. The following list represents the major disputational techniques used during a typical RET session[11]. Notice the correlation between these s and the cognitive errors outlined in the preceding section.

Beliefs are not facts; they are hypotheses ...[and]...are testable and challengeable (Ellis, et. al. 1988, p. 6).

1. **REALITY TESTING**: Have the client question the evidence; are the client's statements true?

2. **FUTURE PACING**: Show clients how they are exaggerating an anticipated consequence. This can be accomplished by having the client fantasize the outcome.

3. **EVALUATING**: Have the client list the advantages and disadvantages of holding on to specific beliefs.

4. **REFRAMING**: Help the client identify positive outcomes that result from events perceived as "bad".

5. **LABELING**: Teach clients to label their irrational processes that result in distortions of reality.

6. **DEPERSONALIZING**: Point out words that have private or "idiosyncratic" meanings to the client to lessen their impact.

7. **ACCEPTING RESPONSIBILITY**: Help clients explain events more accurately by ascribing appropriate responsibility and removing tendency to self-blame.

8. **CREATING ALTERNATIVES**: Assist clients to conceptualize alternative ways to think and behave in the problem situations.

9. **EXAGGERATING**: Point out how foolish a belief is by exaggerating it or demonstrating the paradox of its existence.

10. **VISUALIZING**: Help clients construct imagery they can use to practice new constructive thoughts and rational beliefs.

11. **POLARIZED ROLE PLAYING**: Demonstrate the lack of support for an irrational belief by having the client argue for the belief while the therapist takes the opposing position.

12. **MAKING POSITIVE AFFIRMATIONS**: Ask clients to rehearse rational self-statements.

As we have seen, there are a number of similarities between the Meta Model and other cognitive-behavioral models of change. RET describes a number of "irrational thoughts". One of these is known as *demandingness* which the client demonstrates by using words such as "should", "must", "ought to", "have to", etc. In these cases, an RET therapist will often challenge the client's position using *functional analysis* or *functional disputing*. As described by Ellis (Ellis, et. al., 1988), this disputational process helps the client to see that the emotion resulting from such a belief "...usually doesn't feel good and, even when it does, it brings them less pleasure than pain" (p. 6). Through such insight, the client is able to identify such beliefs as unreasonable, making them easier to discard.

Demandingness is similar to the Meta Model category of Model Operators of Necessity. As stated in *Magic of NLP Demystified*, model operators "...define the boundaries of the person's model of the world. To extend beyond these boundaries is to invite some *catastrophic expectation* over which the speaker believes he has no control. Bringing this expectation into the conscious awareness of the speaker enables him to test and evaluate its validity. If the limit is found to be unreasonable, the boundaries can be removed from that portion of the speaker's model of the world. This process gives the speaker more choices about his thoughts and feelings. It expands his awareness and allows him to develop alternative behaviors in response to similar situations."[12]

As described above, then, the goals of challenging a client's Meta Model violations parallel the RET goals of disputing his irrational thoughts. Where the RET therapist "...helps clients see that their demandingness is unfounded, counterproductive, and irrational" (Ellis, et. al., 1988, p. 7), the NLP practitioner assists the client through a process that brings his catastrophic expectations into conscious awareness which, as noted above, "...enables him to test and evaluate its validity." This process of testing the validity of one's beliefs is critical to the success of the cognitive intervention. What follows is a simple and direct technique developed by Dr. Maxie Maultsby, the originator of Rational Behavior Therapy. Over the past few years, I have found that this is one of the more easily learned and pragmatic examples of this process.

FIVE RATIONAL QUESTIONS OF RBT

Maultsby's Rational Behavior Therapy assists the client in challenging irrational thoughts using what he calls the *five rational questions*. His goal is to assist clients to adjust their thinking towards better emotional health. Maultsby (1984) defines emotionally healthy people as "...reality oriented and...committed to living productive lives with maximum personal and social approval and minimal undesirable emotional conflict" (p. 14). An RBT therapist who uncovers irrational thoughts — usually by having the client work *backwards* from some unpleasant emotion — teaches the client to challenge them using the five rational questions. From Maultsby, 1984, p. 104, these are:

1. Is my thinking here factual?

2. Will my thinking here best help me protect my life and health?

3. Will my thinking here best help me achieve my short-term and long-term goals?

4. Will my thinking here best help me avoid my most undesirable conflicts with others?

5. Will my thinking here best help me feel the emotions I want to feel?

The client is taught that three "no's" to the above set of questions constitutes an irrational thought or belief. Once brought to light, the client gains invaluable insight and choice over future situations where this thought is likely to cause emotional distress. Maultsby's response to the "should's" coming from a client is very plainly spelled out in his delightful self-help booklet *You and Your Emotions* (Maultsby and Hendricks, 1974). In this booklet he describes how the client can change self-defeating thoughts filled with "irrational should's" to the more healthy thinking represented by the following: "I can calmly accept the fact that each person *should* follow his or her own mind because that's all they can do. If others disagree with me, then I can try to influence them to change their minds, and I'll usually do a much better job of influencing them if I refuse to get upset, angry and depressed" (p. 107).

This approach can be contrasted with Beck's cognitive therapy approach where there are only three basic questions taught to the client (DeRubeis and Beck, 1988). These are, "(1) 'What is the evidence for and against the belief?' (2) 'What are alternative interpretations of the event or situation?' and (3) 'What are the real implications, if the belief is correct?'" (p. 183). While not as direct as Maultsby's five rational questions, they serve a similar function to stimulate active interpretation of a belief by the client in order to determine its validity or value.

THE COOKIE-CUTTER MIND

Cognitive distortions, whether evidenced by linguistic patterns or thought processes, are filters through which we perceive and understand the world around us. Much like a cookie cutter, our cognitions shape our experience and powerfully influence our feelings and actions. The filters of distorted cognitions act much like our sensory system which also systematically deletes and distorts information from the world around us.

Humans can hear only within a specific range of sound. We can't, for example, hear a simple dog whistle. Our nervous system – our auditory system specifically – because of its limitations, deletes that data, and it never even registers on our awareness. We know the sound is there, because we can measure it with instruments and see its effects on Fido, but we can't hear it.

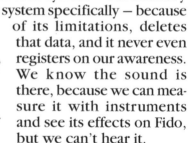

COOKIE-CUTTER MIND

In the same fashion, someone with a tendency towards dichotomous thinking is unlikely to see the gradations of success that can be so helpful to stay motivated to keep trying. Although these approximations of success are measurable and may even be having a profound effect on those around the client, the dichotomous thinker will systematically filter out all evidence short of total success. Likewise, a client who habitually uses the word "can't" – the Meta Model violation called a modal operator of possibility – will also filter out any evidence to the contrary.

It isn't until they are challenged that our clients begin to make shifts in their perceptions that are less limiting and more healthy. The wonderful thing to me about all this is that the various techniques described here become cookie cutters for us, the therapists. The more you know about these approaches, the larger and more varied becomes the edge of your cutter. Because portions of each of the models overlap, the therapist has a variety of techniques from which to choose. And when limitations of one model are discovered, another model can be applied in its place. Let's look at an example that demonstrates an area of overlap.

The client makes the statement, "I should be able to drink like everyone else."

Although there are a number of Meta Model violations in this statement (modal operator of necessity, unspecified verb, generalized referential index), let's look at how the NLP practitioner would challenge the modal operator of necessity, the word "should."

Therapist: *"What would happen if you were not able to drink like everyone else?"*

Client: *"But I don't want that."*

Therapist: *"So, what would happen if you discovered you were not able to drink like everyone else?"*

Client: *"Then I guess I would have to make some changes I don't want to make.*

Therapist: *"What changes specifically?"*

Client: *"For one, I'd have to figure out another way to relax, to unwind at the end of the day."*

Notice the therapist stays with the challenge until the client faces it. The "catastrophic expectation" that arises is multifaceted, but often directly related to the process of *change*. The client is afraid to change (aren't we all, just a little!?), but as the process is explored during the therapy session, it is demystified. The client begins to feel some self-efficacy over his life, and new concrete therapeutic goals can be established.

The RET therapist will take a somewhat different tact, challenging the irrational belief underlying the statement.

Therapist: *"Why* must *you be able to drink like everyone else?"*

Client: *"Because I want to, especially when I'm down."*

Therapist: *"Why should you get everything you want?"*

Client: *"Because it makes me feel better."*

Therapist: *"So, prove that you* have to *feel better by drinking."*

Client: *"Well, it's important to feel good, isn't it?"*

Therapist: *"Let's try this: show me the evidence that you* have to *get whatever you want and that drinking will always result in your feeling better."*

Client: *"Well, in those terms, I guess there really isn't any evidence that I* have to *get whatever I want. And I don't really* have to *drink, even when I want to."*

Therapist: *"Let's use that last statement as one of your new thoughts. I want you to repeat* forcefully *to yourself over and over, 'I don't* have to *drink, even when I want to."*

Again, the therapist dogmatically sticks with the challenge until the client begins to make the shift. At that point, the therapist uses the client's own statement to reinforce the shift in thinking towards a more realistic reality.

The RBT therapist will use yet another tool for facilitating the therapeutic process. Using the five rational questions, the client is led through the disputational process and taught rational thinking at the same time.

Therapist: *"Let's use the five rational questions to explore that thought. Now, is that thought* factual? *Is it an absolute fact that you* should *be able to drink like everyone else?"*

Client: *"Well, no, I guess it isn't factual. It is something I want, but it isn't a fact."*

Therapist: *"OK, now, is that thought going to help you protect your life or health?"*

Client: *"Actually, the doctor says that I've already done some damage to my liver. That's not good. I want to drink like all my friends, but the doctor says I should quit for my health, so I guess the answer to that question is 'no'."*

Therapist: *"Will that thought help you achieve your short or long term goals?"*

Client: *"I'm in this program to help me with a drinking problem. I guess a thought like that isn't going to be very helpful, is it?"*

Therapist: *"No, it isn't. What about the fourth rational question: Will that thought help you avoid undesirable conflicts with others?"*

Client: *"On the surface, it doesn't seem to apply. But if that thought leads me back to drinking like I was, my husband will probably leave me."*

Therapist: *"OK, we already have the three 'no's', so this only adds to it. You can see where this line of questioning is leading. What about the last question: Will this thought help you feel the emotions you want to feel?"*

Client: *"It makes me feel depressed. I don't want to feel depressed, so the answer is 'no' here, too,"*

Therapist: *"You answered all five questions 'no', so the thought is not rational. What is a rational thought you can put in its place that you would be willing to practice?"*

From here the therapist helps the client construct a thought that will lead to more healthy emotions and behaviors. This thought is then practiced regularly using visualization exercises until it becomes what Maultsby (1984) calls a new "emotional habit".

The above examples demonstrate the rich variety of approaches available in the field of cognitive-behavioral therapy. Of course, they are not all-inclusive. There are other equally viable approaches. My goal here, however, is to simply show alternative methods with the idea to expand our therapeutic "bag of tricks" just a little. In the next chapter we will look at how these approaches work with beliefs.

NOTES FOR CHAPTER 5

1. Ellis, et. al. (1988) claim that a review of the RET practice literature supports their contention that "...clients are more likely to be open to a persuasive and directive approach such as RET when they have established trust and confidence in the therapist" (p. 39).

2. See, for example, Lewis and Pucelik (1982), Bandler and Grinder (1975, 1979).

3. Two excellent examples of mapping representational systems can be found in Lewis and Pucelik (1982) and Bandler and Grinder (1979). I have included examples of the behaviors observed during mapping strategies in Appendix 2: NLP Accessing Cues.

4. Anchoring, pacing and leading are techniques utilized by NLP practitioners to facilitate the client's responsiveness to the session. Anchoring is classical conditioning wherein the therapist pairs some neutral stimulus such as a touch or gesture to a specific thought or feeling the client has. Later, that thought or feeling can be brought back using this touch or gesture as a "reminder". Pacing occurs when the therapist's s match the client's perceptions or thoughts, while leading is the process of assisting the client to alter his perceptions, thoughts or feelings. These techniques are thoroughly described in Bandler & Grinder (1975a) and Grinder & Bandler (1981).

5. Another aspect of the use of negations in our language has to do with *how* that type of information is coded and processed by our brains. If I tell my daughter, "Don't knock the milk off the table," in order to understand the direction, she must go through a complex cognitive sequence that starts with some representation of herself *knocking the milk off the table*. Once that has been processed, then the negative can be added, and the direction followed. But it is that momentary "rehearsal" at a deep unconscious level of the event that I am asking her to prevent that is disconcerting as I squat down to wipe up the ensuing mess. It would be much more constructive for me to say, "Keep your elbow *away* from that milk," where her mental rehearsal will naturally compliment my intentions!

6. *From Frogs into Princes*, Bandler and Grinder (1979, page 70). The complete Meta Model is presented in their first NLP text, *The Structure of Magic, Vol I* (Bandler and Grinder, 1975b) and an easy-to-learn version can be found in *Magic of NLP Demystified* (Lewis & Pucelik, 1982).

7. There is a nice discussion of *neurotic projection* in his last book (Perls, 1973) which was edited by Richard Bandler.

8. One approach to cognitive therapy, originally proposed by Aron Beck (see the next section) is described under the category of "irrational thoughts" by Persons (1989). She concludes that fear often underlies "should" statements and they often bring about negative emotions and behaviors. Although less systematic than Maultsby or NLP, she prescribes both challenging the irrational thinking by disputing the obvious inconsistencies and also educating the client to the rationale behind "why" some things are or are not the way they are.

9. An exceptionally readable discussion of cognitive therapy by DeRubeis and Beck (1988) outlines the six cognitive errors in their chapter in *Handbook of cognitive-behavioral therapies.*

10. I have taken liberties in adapting the list that follows from the "Commonly Observed Cognitive Distortions" outlined in Freeman, et. al. (1990), p. 5.

11. This list is paraphrased (and I have added my own labels for each technique) from Ellis, et. al. (1988, p. 57). These authors cite A. Freeman, "Cognitive Therapy: An Overview," in A. Freeman & V. Greenwood (Eds.), *Cognitive Therapy: Application in Psychiatric and Medical Setting*, Human Science Press, New York, 1987, as the source for the original list.

12. Lewis and Pucelik (1982, p. 93).

IRRATIONAL BELIEFS

...the most elegant and long-lasting

changes that humans can effect are ones

that involve philosophic restructuring

of irrational beliefs

(Ellis and Dryden, 1987, p. 24-25).

A perusal of literature in the field of cognitive-behavioral therapy shows the terms *schema, dysfunctional* or *irrational belief* and *underlying assumption* are used interchangeably to "...refer to the individual's unspoken, and often unrecognized, assumptions" (Freeman, et. al., 1990, p.4).[1] Most of us know from experience that these assumptions are usually at the core of the problems that dogmatically impede therapeutic change in our clients. Unless we are able to impact these beliefs in therapy, our best efforts are likely to fail.

BELIEFS ABOUT BELIEFS

Each of the various approaches within the field of cognitive-behavioral therapy have somewhat different slants on the concept of beliefs. RET, for example, defines beliefs as, "...cognitions, thoughts, attitudes, self-statements, or images...[that] are the primary determinants of emotions" (Ellis, et. al. 1988, p.6). DeRubeis and Beck (1988) describe "...underlying cognitive structures that organize the client's experience..." (p. 275). They call them *core beliefs* and posit that certain of these schemata cause clients their emotional distress.

The cognitive therapist Marvin Goldfried (1989), on the other hand, defines *schema* as "...a cognitive representation of one's past experiences with situations or people..." (p. x). He goes on to describe how this "prototypical abstraction of a complex concept", or what we might consider a *template*, is used by individuals to shape their perceptions, organize new information and eventually guide the person's feelings and behavior. This is the "cookie cutter mind" concept discussed in the last chapter. Those familiar with my previous book (Lewis & Pucelik, 1982) will recognize similarities between this description and our representation of *constraints on our models of the world*[2].

Goldfried's description also echoes the work of Dilts (1990) who defines beliefs as "closely held generalizations" (p. 215) about the world and our place in it. These include generalizations about cause and effect relationships, the meanings and relationships of things and events, limits or boundaries to our models of the world, and our capabilities and identities. He writes, "A belief is not 'A' picture or 'A' set of words or 'A' feeling, but a relationship among all of them" (p. 77). Beliefs appear to operate at a logical level one step higher than internal dialogue or other "capability" strategies the client uses. Because beliefs operate at a different level of human functioning than behavior, if we are to change them, we will have to utilize different interventions than we would use when working with behaviors.

Cognitive-behavioral therapists use specific disputational techniques as shown in the previous chapter to lead a client to understand the irrationality of dysfunctional beliefs. Maultsby (1984), for example, utilizes an ingenious technique to assist his clients in differentiating between beliefs and reality. He demonstrates how a belief may not be factual by showing a man attempting to stand atop a chair which he "believes" will support him. When the chair collapses, Maultsby points out, it demonstrates that belief and fact are not necessarily one and the same. Maultsby makes a further distinction, describing *beliefs* as spoken (although usually unconscious) forms of habitually paired perceptions and thoughts, while *attitudes* are the unspoken forms of those same cognitive units.

It appears generally true that CBT therapists see beliefs as cognitive structures composed of internal images, self-statements (often reflected in automatic thoughts), and other processes that mediate emotions and other behaviors. Regardless of the particular definition of belief adhered to by the therapist, it can be agreed that working with dysfunctional or irrational beliefs forms a major part of the therapeutic relationship. In this chapter, we will explore a variety of approaches the therapist can take to impact this area of human functioning.

IMPACTING BELIEFS

Because of their profound impact on behavior, beliefs form an integral part of the therapeutic interaction. Working to change beliefs is important not only to the ongoing therapy, but also as a means of preventing the client's regressing to old patterns of behavior following termination of therapy. As Freeman, et. al. (1990) put it, "In order to achieve lasting results, it is also important to modify the beliefs and assumptions that predispose the client to his or her problems and to help him or her plan effective ways to handle situations which might precipitate a relapse." Volume II of this series focuses on issues and concerns of relapse prevention[3].

...if people really believe they can't do something, they're going to find an unconscious way to keep the change from occurring. They'll find a way to interpret the results to conform with their existing belief
Dilts, et. al. (1990)

At what level in human functioning do beliefs operate? In Chapter 3, we saw how Dilts (1990) addressed this issue by proposing that humans operate in the world from certain "logical levels". NLP has drawn heavily from the work of Gregory Bateson in the development of many of its models. Bateson (1972) generated his logical categories of learning and communication from Bertrund Russell's "Theory of Logical Types"[4]. For our purposes, this describes how a category at one level may be contained in another category at a "higher logical level", while the contra positive is not true. In other words, a Chevy is a car; however, not all cars are Chevys. Dilts' model delineates six major levels of functioning. From the "bottom-up", they are: perceiving the environment; responding to and on the environment; using mental maps and strategies; using belief systems; operating from personal identity; and operating from spiritual levels. The reason this is so important to the therapist is that the level from which the person is operating to experience a problem will impact how best to treat the dysfunction.

A therapist can work with a client's problem-solving skills, for example, but this work will not necessarily change the client's *beliefs* about his ability to resolve his problems, because these beliefs operate within the client at a higher logical level. Despite all the great work with a therapist, a client who believes he is incapable of changing will ultimately *sabotage* his efforts to maintain the therapeutic gains. On the other hand, working with the client's beliefs has the potential to effect processes at lower logical levels of functioning, such as a person's capabilities at problem-solving. Of course, the client may still require some *remedial skills training* at that level.

Goldfried (1989) proposes a similar concept addressing how a therapist should work with a client. He suggests there are basically two approaches to facilitate change: "top-down" and "bottom-up". The top-down strategies work with the client's cognitions and assume that behavioral change will follow. Bottom-up work proposes that the client must first change his or her behavior in order to alter *core cognitions*. He points out that these two approaches are reminiscent of the old argument between the psychoanalysts who emphasized "insight" and the behaviorists requirement for observable "action". He suggests that effective therapeutic interventions need to operate from both directions at once. Many of the techniques presented on these pages represent this dual approach nicely.

IRRATIONAL STRATEGIES

One useful description of how beliefs effect addiction comes from the Rational Emotive theory of addiction (Ellis, et. al., 1988). What Ellis and his colleagues have done is describe several major *irrational strategies* clients use to acquire and maintain their addictive behaviors. These strategies may operate independently or in combination within a client to cause the irrational behaviors associated with impulse-control disorders such as addiction. I particularly like their model, because it is simple and underscores the self-reinforcing nature of addictive strategies[5].

■ DISCOMFORT ANXIETY

Each of the addictive strategies described in the RET model incorporate an affective state Ellis (1978/1979) calls *discomfort anxiety*. Essentially, this is an emotion a person feels when *anticipating* pain, discomfort, or other unpleasant experience. It is an anxiety that has its source in the clients' irrational belief that they absolutely *must* not or *can't* tolerate such experiences. Discomfort anxiety is the emotional result of a specific strategy or pattern people utilize when confronted with certain kinds of situations. Ellis, et. al. (1988) states, "Most people with impulse-control problems fit into this pattern regardless of the substance or action to which they are addicted."

■ ABSTINENCE ANXIETY

Based on the work of Ellis (1978/1978) and his colleagues (Ellis, et. al. 1988), I have proposed a more specific term called *abstinence anxiety*. At its core is Ellis' "discomfort anxiety"; however, my term applies exclusively to the angst experienced when an addict chooses or is forced to abstain. The creation of abstinence anxiety is the primary cognitive dynamic involved in addictive disorders. This pattern forms what I call the "addiction motor" that seems to drive most addictive disorders as described by Ellis.

ABSTINENCE ANXIETY

Abstinence anxiety starts when the addicted individual perceives some stimulus to use alcohol or drugs or initiate a compulsive mood-altering activity. Normally, the stimulus will cause an internal tension as the addict struggles between conflicting internal thoughts while attempting to make the decision whether or not to use. If the individual is prevented from using (through physical or financial unavailability of the substance or activity, incarceration, or admission to a treatment facility) or by a personal choice to abstain, the stage is set for this cognitive dynamic to be initiated. Once the person begins to refrain from using, there is a sequence of internal cognitive activities which result in the intensely disturbing abstinence anxiety. Of major importance in the formation of this emotional state are certain irrational beliefs that lead to extremely low tolerance for frustration.

■ LFT BELIEFS

Returning to the RET model of addiction, Ellis (1978/1979) proposes that discomfort anxiety is intensified by additional irrational beliefs which cause *low frustration tolerance* (LFT). With addicts and alcoholics, this low frustration tolerance is combined with a firm belief that they are unable to cope without returning to use. There are specific types of irrational beliefs that can lead to low frustration tolerance and result in abstinence anxiety when an addict, alcoholic or compulsive client abstains in situations where they would commonly choose to use. We can categorize these into three perceptual orientations[6]:

A. Beliefs about capabilities (self-efficacy):

- I can't stand not using.

- I can't function without it.

- I'm not strong enough to resist it.

- I can't stand the bad feeling (deprivation) when I want to use.

B. Beliefs about causes (cause-effect):

- I have to use, in order to go on with life, because using makes life bearable.

- I deserve to use because life is too hard.

- I shouldn't abstain, because it feels so good to use.

- I shouldn't abstain because it causes me so much pain.

C. Beliefs about self (identity):

- I am a horribly deprived person if I can't use.

- I have to use to compensate for my difficult life.

- I must use to fit in with my friends.

- I'm an "alchie" (or "druggie", or "head", etc.)

When faced with various events, addicted clients begin to utilize their dysfunctional strategies in an attempt to cope. The beliefs above usually occur as well-rehearsed automatic thoughts and result in the eventual use for relief from abstinence anxiety.

THE SYNTAX OF RET AND RBT

There is a syntax to the RET and RBT explanations of how people cause themselves emotional discomfort called the "ABC's of human emotions." All emotions are initiated by some *activating event* (A) about which a person has some *beliefs* or *thoughts* (B). These thoughts result in an *emotional response* (C-1) which may be followed by some *action* (C-2) based on that response. For example, the basic sequence of events leading to a person's use episode is:

1. **(A)** *Activating event*: The client experiences some stimulus for drinking/using (e.g., passes the local bar, sees a sign for the horse races, smells pizza cooking, feels physical discomfort of withdrawal symptoms, etc.).

2. **(B)** *Beliefs* or *thoughts*: Has thoughts about using, believing it will either be pleasurable or will reduce pain or discomfort.

3. **(C-1)** *Emotions*: Experiences a desire to use, gamble, etc.[7]

4. **(C-2)** *Action*: Begins to drink, use, or engage in compulsive activity.

We can interrupt the strategy above with abstinence. If a person does *not* use in step 4, a new dynamic is initiated that results in abstinence anxiety and low frustration tolerance. The specific sequence of the abstinence anxiety pattern is as follows:

1. **(A)** *Activating event*: In place of Step 4 above, the client decides to abstain or is prevented from using or engaging in the compulsive activity.

2. **(B)** *Beliefs* or *thoughts*: In the face of abstention, the client thinks irrational thoughts, such as the LFT Beliefs listed above.

3. **(C-1)** *Emotions*: These thoughts and beliefs cause abstinence anxiety and result in low frustration tolerance.

4. (C–2) *Action*: The client ends up using or engages in the mood-altering activity in order to decrease the anxiety.

In RET, the above represents a *strategy*[8] a person uses to become and stay addicted. The likelihood of a client being able to abstain when faced with the extreme anxiety and low frustration tolerance is reduced. The abstinence anxiety becomes the "motor" which drives the addictive cycle.

RET therapists suggest that the best way to intervene with compulsive disorders is to *dispute the irrational beliefs* that underlie the emotion that stimulates the person to engage in addictive behaviors. RET then teaches the client alternative thoughts to the irrational beliefs and provides opportunities for the client to practice them on a regular basis. As they arise during the therapy session, during the time between sessions, and during specifically assigned tasks, the client is asked to practice disputing the dysfunctional beliefs and replace them with more rational alternatives. This process can be applied to each of the following addictive strategies.[9]

THE USING-TO-COPE STRATEGY

In this strategy, the client employs irrational beliefs about his ability to cope with certain problems or situations. This strategy, however, actually perpetuates the problem, because the clients tend to succumb to the using behaviors before they have a chance to try any other coping behaviors. This is one of the three types of "interference" with change identified by Dilts, et. al. (1990)[10]. In order to change, a person must learn new skills, new strategies, etc., then must allow time and effort to *practice* these new skills. Most addicts and alcoholics suffer from the need for *immediate gratification*, likely the result of the "quick fix" found in the pills, powders and potions. This attitude tends to be present with many of life's activities. A client's impatience with the change process will almost always need to be addressed by the addictions counselor or therapist.

■ IRRATIONAL COPING BELIEFS:

There are again certain kinds of thoughts and beliefs that help shape and maintain this strategy. Most of these beliefs have to do with a person's sense of control or identity. Some examples of these include:

A. Beliefs about capabilities (self-efficacy):

- I just can't stand being upset in any way.
- I'm not strong enough to handle unpleasant emotions.
- I'm not supposed to get upset.
- I can't deal with difficult situations.

B. Beliefs about causes (cause-effect):

- I shouldn't have to experience the pain of emotional problems.

USING TO COPE

C. Beliefs about self (identity):

- I believe that I must be happy at all times.

- I should never get angry, sad, or upset.

- I'm always the cause of the problem.

■ ADDICTIVE COPING STRATEGY:

As in the previous strategy, the client goes through a specific sequence of events. However, central to this strategy is the client's belief that using or engaging in the compulsive disorder will either "fix" the problem or will remove the emotional distress associated with it. Notice that the "addiction motor" (the abstinence anxiety strategy) perpetuates the client's dependence on mood-altering drugs or activities. The sequence in this avoidance/escape coping pattern is:

1. **(A) *Activating event*:** The client encounters some difficulty or problem.

2. **(B) *Beliefs* or *thoughts*:** Has beliefs or thinks irrational thoughts about the problem such as outlined in the irrational coping beliefs above.

3. **(C–1) *Emotions*:** Becomes emotionally upset about the problem.

The upset emotional state triggers thoughts and beliefs about using as a way of coping with the problem. Obviously, this is based on past experiences of the "escape" provided by the chemical high or some other mood-altering activity. Basically, then, the emotion itself becomes the new activating event for the second part of the strategy:

1. **(A) *Activating event*:** Client's negative emotional state becomes the activating event.

2. **(B) *Beliefs* or *thoughts*:** Has thoughts or beliefs about using to reduce the discomfort of the negative emotions.

3. **(C–1) *Emotions*:** Feels the urge or desire to use.

4. **(C–2) *Action*:** Begins to use or starts the compulsive behavior.

At this point, however, if abstention is either chosen or required, the "addiction motor" sequence is initiated, and the steps of the abstinence anxiety strategy are followed. Because the intense discomfort anxiety is associated with abstention, it will recur in all the addictive disorders. And, because there is such low tolerance for frustration, if left untreated, the combination almost guarantees a return to use. This is one of the reasons addictive behaviors are so difficult to extinguish or change.

THE WORTHLESS RELAPSER STRATEGY

At various times during the addictive process, and especially during the later stages, the compulsive user regularly battles with him or herself, attempting to either control or quit the compulsion. Because this so frequently ends in failure, the consequent emotions are bound to involve the person's sense of self-efficacy or self-esteem. At the end of "another" binge, or even simply as he or she hoists the first glass, the old struggle erupts. As the first sip slides down the throat, in the anguish of defeat, the sober self throws down the gauntlet and begins the tedious task of recreating the remorse necessary to galvanize the person back on a road that at least looks like it is heading towards sobriety.

■ IRRATIONAL BELIEFS ABOUT SELF:

Most of the irrational thoughts involved in this strategy involve beliefs about self (beliefs about identity). Some of the thoughts that perpetuate this pattern include:

- People who can't control their use are weak and worthless.

- I'm an addict/alcoholic/gambler, therefore I can't stop.

- I should be able to quit easily.

- I must quit, because if I don't, I'm not worth a damn.

- Now I know I'm a looser, since I failed again.

■ **WORTHLESS RELAPSER STRATEGY**:

Following the use episode, the addict begins to utilize labels and other irrational cognitions to describe himself. The sequence for achieving and maintaining this cycle of depression is:

WORTHLESS RELAPSER

1. **(A)** *Activating event*: The client uses after deciding to abstain or quit.

2. **(B)** *Beliefs* or *thoughts*: Has irrational thoughts about the use episode such as those above.

3. **(C-1)** *Emotions*: Feels emotionally distressed, depressed, guilty, angry, etc.

Following the use episode, and as a result of the irrational thoughts noted above, the client begins to fantasize using again to relieve the emotional distress – the guilt, shame, depression, etc. This is identical to the Coping Strategy in that the return to use is irrationally seen as the "salve" to heal the hurt.

1. **(A)** *Activating event*: Client feels emotionally dis-

tressed over recent use episode, and this emotional state becomes the activating event.

2. **(B)** *Beliefs* or *thoughts*: Thinks about using because he believes it will eliminate the distress.

3. **(C–1)** *Emotions*: Has the irrational thought that using will end the discomfort.

4. **(C–2)** *Action*: Begins to use or starts the compulsive disorder to obtain relief.

At this stage, the 'addiction motor" kicks in if the addict tries to abstain, and the cycle repeats itself. These two cycles, the coping strategy and the worthless relapser strategy, will continue to operate within an individual until they are interrupted by interventions that impact the client's dysfunctional beliefs about him or herself and the irrational belief that the drug or activity is a positive means of coping with the guilt or shame.

One special problem associated with this strategy pointed out by Ellis, et. al. (1988), is the what is called the *abstinence violation effect* (AVE). Basically, this is the belief that a small lapse will *inevitably* lead to a return to use (relapse) over which the person is powerless. The person who, in a moment of "sanity" discovers the first half of a drink already gone, will choose to continue drinking rather than stopping at that point as a direct result of this belief. This may be in large part due to the "labeling" clients do ("I'm a drunk. I'll always be a drunk.") which supports the belief that one drink will result in a loss of control (the famous AA slogan "A drink, a drunk" fits in here as well).[11]

THE EXCITEMENT IMPERATIVE STRATEGY

The final RET strategy arises from the observation by Ellis and his colleagues that a high percentage of substance abusers and those addicted to mood-altering activities appear to have a specific personality disorder, the antisocial personality. It is statistically relevant that a large percentage of crimes are committed while under the influence of drugs and alcohol, and criminal activity is often associated with this disorder. My personal experience counseling addicts showed that even the act of "boosting" (stealing to support a habit) is considered a pleasurable high by many of these individuals. This may account for the apparent high occurrence of certain psychopathic disorders found among many addicts and alcoholics in recovery.

■ ANTISOCIAL BELIEFS:

Not all thoughts and beliefs listed below are "antisocial". However, these are typical of individuals operating with a strategy that requires excitement or stimulation in their lives.

EXCITEMENT IMPERATIVE

Some of the beliefs associated with this strategy are:

- I can't stand being bored.

- Drugs and alcohol make an instant party.

- Life without drugs/alcohol is boring.

- People who don't use are dead-heads.

- It's cool to use.

- I must have some excitement in my life.

- Gamblers/drinkers/addicts lead fast and colorful lives.

■ THE EXCITEMENT IMPERATIVE STRATEGY:

The sequence for this psychopathic "high sensation" seeking pattern is:

1. **(A)** *Activating event*: The client notices he or she is bored.

2. **(B)** *Beliefs* or *thoughts*: Thinks the irrational thoughts or beliefs above.

3. **(C-1)** *Emotions*: Has the urge to drink/use/boost/ etc. for excitement.

4. **(C-2)** *Action*: Drinks or uses.

As with the previous strategies, if the individual is prevented from using or decides to abstain, the abstinence anxiety sequence is initiated resulting in a return to use. In each of the above scenarios, the client generally perceives him or herself as incapable of changing. Through the use of the disputational techniques described in the previous chapter, and the 9 disputational strategies below, the therapist leads the client to understand the irrationality of such beliefs. Working with the therapist, new more healthy alternatives are generated, and the client is given homework assignments to ensure that they are regularly practiced.

NINE DISPUTATION STRATEGIES OF RET

I have taken some liberties with the disputational strategies listed in Ellis, et. al. (1988). What follows, however, is based on their work.

1. DISTORTIONS
Dispute the irrational belief and show how it distorts reality. This is where such tools as the Meta Model covered in the previous chapter can be extremely useful.

2. TESTING
Show how, if the irrational belief were true, certain deductions could be made about the world, then help the client "empirically test" these deductions.

The therapist may employ guided fantasy, provide ordinary examples from life, or simply have the client recall experiences/events/situations that demonstrate the illogic of the belief.

3. NEGATIVE ORIENTATION
Demonstrate how the irrational belief can explain important negative events in the client's life, while lacking evidence of explanation for other events. Using basic logical arguments, the client is assisted in changing his or her perceptions of the belief in question.

4. DIRECT EFFECTS
Help clients experience how maintaining the irrational belief has helped or hurt them. One of the best approaches utilizes the client's own motivation for entering treatment. The therapist can help the client see how certain beliefs led naturally to the emotions and behaviors that resulted in the need for treatment.

5. REPETITION
Repeat steps 1–4 as many times as necessary to convince the client that the irrational belief is false or self-defeating. We have the tendency to tenaciously hold on to our beliefs. They are, after, the very fabric of our perceptual paradigms! Patience is an important ingredient in disputational therapies.

6. REPLACEMENT
Help the client create a new rational belief that can be used in situations in place of the irrational belief. It is important for the client to be fully involved in this process. When a client either cannot or will not participate, some of the following NLP techniques may be more practical and effective.

7. ECOLOGICAL CHECK
Be sure to explore the new rational belief for logical fallacies. Be alert, too, for what the NLPers call the "ecological check". That is, make sure the *whole* client agrees with the new belief; otherwise, he or she may unconsciously work to sabotage the positive outcomes of the work.

8. TEST
As in 2 above, make deductions from the new rational belief and test these deductions to see if they

lead to more accurate predictions about the world than the old irrational belief. Again, personal experiences, guided fantasy, and other techniques can be employed effectively here.

9. **FUTURE PACE**

Show the client how changing to new rational beliefs will positively affect their emotions and actions. I cannot stress enough the value of *client expectations* to the outcome of therapy. The more the client fully understands and believes that a new strategy will work, the more likely it will work and work quickly. The therapist needs to spend some time building up the client's expectations of success. This can be done overtly or using more covert techniques (such as metaphor or embedded suggestions, for example).

THE GOAL OF RET

The goal of such interventions is to provide the client with motivation to change his or her irrational beliefs. Using the "stages of motivation" model discussed in chapter 3, the therapist takes an educational approach to draw the client from precontemplation to contemplation and then towards the decision to change. At first, the therapist attempts to create doubt in the mind of the client about his/her current irrational beliefs. This is accomplished by demonstrating that such beliefs not only do not help the client solve problems, but in most cases actually exacerbate them. At that point, the therapist helps build new beliefs to take the place of the old dysfunctional ones and helps the client plan how to implement these new strategies in his or her ongoing life.[12]

■ COGNITIVE-BEHAVIORAL HOMEWORK

Most CBT therapists employ some kind of homework, both to increase the client's awareness of specific patterns of thought and to test new hypothesis and reinforce therapeutic gains made during the sessions. DeRubeis and Beck (1988) note that Beck is credited with developing a tool known as the 'Daily Record of Dysfunctional Thoughts" or DRDT. The client fills out five sections of the record in response to certain events. The sections include 1) the situation, 2) the emotion(s), 3) the automatic thought(s), 4) the rational response, and 5) the outcome. This is very similar to Maultsby's (1984) "Written Rational Self-Analysis (RSA) in which the client fills out six sections, including, 1) the activating event, 2) beliefs and thoughts about the event, 3) consequence of the beliefs and thoughts, 4) a "camera check" of the activating event, 5) rational debate of the beliefs and thoughts, and 6) expected new behaviors.

Most of my actual treatment process in RET consists of active-directive cognitive debating – with emotive and behavioral homework always integrally included but with a strong emphasis on helping clients achieve a profound – and preferably quite conscious – philosophic or attitudinal change. Ellis (1989)

With either of these tools, the therapist can fulfill two major functions. First, as an educational tool, these steps teach the client to attend to thoughts and responses to situations in a different way than they have in the past. As DeRubeis and Beck (1988) point out, the client is the expert on his or her own internal processes. These tools help the client become more aware of these processes so that they can be addressed during therapy.

Second, the process of completing these forms teaches the client basic disputational strategies. They also serve as a means to both motivate client participation in learning these therapeutic strategies and monitor client progress along the way.

Maultsby (1975, 1984) also credits himself with developing a particularly effective form of therapeutic rehearsal he calls *rational emotive imagery* (REI). Following the generation of a new set of beliefs using his standard RSA format, Maultsby has his clients relax, visualize the situation that initiated the irrational thoughts and beliefs (activating event), then picture themselves saying the new rational thoughts and feeling the desired emotions resulting in the desired actions[13].

Beliefs are strategies a person uses to operate in the world. They are a templates we use to shape our perceptions, and they influence our emotions and motivate our behavior. Beliefs help us function in our complex society where simple cause-effect relationships and more basal instincts don't always work. The CBT techniques we have been exploring tend to meet the belief head on, galvanizing the client's current resources and abilities to take rational evidence and dispute the dysfunctional beliefs that are limiting or pain-producing. Then they assist the client to create more rational belief strategies to take their place. NLP takes another tact, opting instead to intervene at the original *source* of the belief and then creating a new experience that incorporates the positive intentions of the old belief into a more useful and functional strategy.

NLP APPROACHES

Dilts' techniques for working with beliefs (Dilts, 1990; Dilts, et. al., 1990) reflect a theoretical basis for the therapeutic process that is quite different from the above approaches. Rather than focusing on the *content* of a belief, NLP generally focuses on the *structure* or *function* of the belief. To do this, the NLP practitioner has been trained to observe *minimal cues*, minute changes in the physiology of clients as they think and communicate. These include eye accessing cues, changes in posture, breathing and gestures which are associated with specific strategies or thoughts (see Appendix 2 for the complete descriptions). As the therapist maps out the specific sequence of "internal events" the client demonstrates while thinking about or discussing a particular belief, the structure can be analyzed and compared to more functional strategies. Based on this analysis, a new more functional belief is created with the client to replace the irrational belief.

NLP sees beliefs as perceived relationships between aspects of the client's past experience. While there are other categories, there appear to be three types of beliefs important to the addictions counselor. The first category includes beliefs that are utilized to guide current behavior and shape the client's perceptions regarding his or her *capabilities*. These are beliefs about what the client can or can't do, and often involve the Meta Model violation of modal operators of possibility. The second include beliefs related to the client's perceptions of *cause-effect relationships*. These beliefs concern how the environment (including other people) affects the client, and how the client affects others. Mind reading and modal operators of necessity along with the cause-effect Meta Model violations are often associated with these thoughts. The last category involves beliefs related directly to *self-perception*. These are the beliefs about "who I am" in the world. We are likely to find labeling and other generalizations in this category. Regardless of their type, it is the beliefs that block positive growth or cause unnecessary, unrealistic, or unproductive emotional distress that need to be addressed in therapy.

Dysfunctional beliefs are often the result of some traumatic event that occurred during the client's childhood. During the course of a session working with the NLP techniques that follow, you may find the client remembering bits and pieces of dialogue from significant people in their lives at or around the event. There may be visual memories and very powerful emotions as well. Some will be more clear than others. The goal is to completely sort out the experience with each representation (visual, auditory, and kinesthetic) isolated and distinct. Next the therapist helps the client identify the *positive intention* of each part of the belief so that a new belief can be created to fulfill the same function *constructively* rather than dysfunctionally.

BELIEF MOLECULES

Dilts (1990) likens the whole belief to a "molecule" made up of visual, auditory and kinesthetic aspects of the original experience. Let's take a look at how, at the most basic level of intervention, a single belief can be mapped and then altered to better fit the client's needs. In our example in this section, we will look at a client's beliefs about his capabilities. Since a sense of self-efficacy is closely related to a client's willingness to attempt to do things, beliefs about capabilities provide important opportunities for intervention. If a client doesn't believe that visualizations or positive affirmations will work, then they probably won't, regardless of the finesse with which the therapist constructs them. This principle is the opposite of the "placebo" effect, where the client believes the "sugar pill" will cure the illness, and it does. In that case, regardless of the technique utilized, the client's *belief in it* is the curative factor.

■ DYSFUNCTIONAL BELIEF STATEMENTS

In the examples below, identifying the belief to be worked with simply requires the therapist to pay attention to the client's statements about his or her capabilities relative to the desired state or goal. Common statements that indicate underlying dysfunctional beliefs include:

- I can't stay sober.
- I always fail to meet my expectations.
- I can't complete anything.
- Recovery only works if you want it to.
- Can't teach an old dog new tricks.

Once the client has made such a statement, you start the process by pressing the client to describe or label the underlying belief. You can ask Meta Model questions such as "What stops/prevents you?" or "What do you think would happen if you did 'X'?" You might utilize some of the RET disputational techniques previously discussed.

During an interview, a client repeated several times the statement, "I can't stay sober?" The therapist chose to ask the Meta Model question, "What stops you from staying sober?" What is important in the NLP process described below, however, is not so much what our client *said* as it is *what he did* with his physiology. While he was thinking about how to respond to the therapist's question, the therapist mapped out his minimal cues and *anchored*[14] the belief for future reference. Drawing primarily from the work of Dilts on belief systems (Dilts, 1990; Dilts, et. al., 1990), the following describes how the therapist would continue the intervention.

■ STEP 1: IDENTIFYING THE BELIEF

The first step is to identify the dysfunctional belief "molecule". This entails identifying each of the sensory representations of the belief. In our example above, the client stops, looks up and to his left (visual remembered accessing cue) and says, "I don't know." Then he shifts, sighs deeply and hangs his head, saying, "Every time I try I fail." While it is noteworthy that the client fails at his attempts to abstain, the important communication in this case is *nonverbal*. The critical piece of information is his quick glance up and to the left. This accessing cue provides the NLP practitioner the "key" into the locked "black box" that used to confound the behaviorists some years ago. With this process, we can now uncover one of the unconscious strategies which negatively impacts this client's attempts to successfully achieve his goal.

Using this piece of information, the thera- pist might say, "I noticed you looked up just before you answered. That usually means you had an image of something in your mind. Can you describe for me what that was?" While the client generates his response, the therapist observes to see that the physiology repeats itself. In other words, he watches to see if a pattern emerges. The client again looks up and to the left, sighs, hangs his head down and says, "I don't know. I just get depressed thinking about it."

What a marvelous confirmation that there is indeed a strategy at work here! The task, then, is to unravel this out-of-awareness pattern the client has success-

What stops you?

I don't Know.

IDENTIFY THE BELIEF

fully utilized to help ensure he fails at sobriety. What we often find with irrational beliefs is that the client has "mixed up" his internal resources. The end state in this example is that when he thinks about sobriety he finds himself *feeling depressed*. We need to help him sort out the confusion.

■ STEP 2: SORT THE REPRESENTATIONS

The next step in the process requires the client to dissociate each of the overlapping representational systems. The "contamination" of the representations within belief molecules is easily observed in the *synesthesia* the client displays — talking about a feeling while visualizing an image, or creating distressful images from self-talk are common examples. The separation and sorting of the representations will greatly assist the client in identifying positive aspects of the experience. This is accom- plished by having the client access each representation (from the "correct" accessing position — see appendix 3) one at a time while talking about what is happening in each.

The therapist has the client in our example sit in the visual accessing posture, eyes up and to the left, instructing him to sit straight and breathe higher in the chest (shallow), then asks him again to form the visual image. The therapist may need to use *sub-modalities*[15] to assist the client to "tune in" the image.

Of course, the therapist may choose to start with the feeling of "depression", asking the client to sit with head down, sigh deeply and describe what he is aware of. From this feeling the rest of the pattern can be generated. The therapist might ask what internal words he is aware of:

"The words I keep hearing, over and over are, 'You can't do it, because you've tried and failed. Why bother when you know nothing will change.'"

Then the tone of voice; "Is that your voice or someone else's you hear?":

SORT THE REPRESENTATION

"You know, that almost sounds like my mother's voice."

Each representation needs to be cleanly sorted. "Now let's see if we can identify that image.":

"I think that the image I keep seeing is my mother's face. She looks upset with me."

It is important to note that these images and words will generally be aspects of some experience or experiences from the client's past. Some of these memories are vivid and clear, while others remain vague, confused and defocused. They all relate in some way to the irrational belief, and it is this *relationship* that the therapist attempts to uncover. In the next chapter we will go into the origins of these beliefs in much greater depth.

■ STEP 3: IDENTIFY POSITIVE INTENTIONS

In this step, the therapist starts by asking the client to think about the desired goal. The easiest way is to have him visually construct an image of the goal by accessing up and right. Once there is a clear image of the desired goal, the therapist returns to the dialog established with each of the separate representations of the limiting belief. What is the image the client originally made trying to *communicate* to him in relation to his desired goal? Within his irrational belief, what are his kinesthetic sensations communicating regarding the goal? What are his internal dialog or other verbal experiences trying to communicate? By opening this dialog with each of these parts separately, you *pace* them in preparation to eventually *lead*[16] them to a more positive outcome. Here, the task is to one at a time identify the *positive intention* of each of these representations *in relation to the client's desired goal.*

In our example, the client pictures himself still sober a few months down the road. Now the therapist asks him to access the image of his mother and asks, "What is it that image of your mother is trying to communicate to you? That image seems to pop up whenever you think about staying sober. What is it's *intention*? How is it trying to *help* you?" The idea here is to help the client frame the rationale of each representation in *positive* terms.

The client begins to communicate with that part or aspect of himself, eventually identifying the goal of that part: "She looks upset, because she wants me to take care of myself, but she's afraid I might get frustrated and give up too soon." The auditory part has a similar intention: the words are to protect him from being disappointed if he does fail. Here, of course, he can be assisted in creating a more useful set of words, such as "I know you can do it. It will just take some time." Separating the tone of voice from the words, the client discovers that it "...actually sounds encourag-ing, like she's coaxing me on." Finally, when he accesses his feelings, instead of depression, he finds a mixture of fear and excitement. This can be reframed into "anticipation" of the event or the changes that will occur in order to achieve the desired goal.

IDENTIFY POSITIVE INTENTIONS

■ STEP 4: BALANCING ECOLOGICAL INTEGRITY

One of the premises of NLP is that each piece of a strategy has an important function. Just as the automatic self-talk identified by CBT has the power to control the behaviors of an individual, NLP expands the idea to include each of the sensory representations. Each of these "parts" works both independently and in concert. You might say that there is *value* in every part. What happens in dysfunctional strategies is that the *positive intention* of the parts becomes lost or is misinterpreted, and results in a problematic end state. Because the process takes place at a completely unconscious level, however, the client is helpless to change it. If we simply override the representations that appear negative, we run the risk of upsetting the *ecological integrity* of the system. This would result in a temporary or surface change in behavior that would return to the old strategy after a time or under stress.

In this step, the various parts of the irrational belief are asked to provide input towards the client's goal. In this way, they continue to be valuable *resources*. The subtle modification of the client's goal validates each of the parts of the system and provides outlet for their energies. This also has the additional advantage of preventing potential sabotaging by a part that has not been reintegrated into the system.

With the help of the therapist, the client reviews each of the memories for information that can be used to modify the original goal. How do the visual images or the remembered voices of the client's parent *connect* with the goal? What can the client learn *today* about those connections with past experiences? This generates a *feedback loop* between the goal and the components of the belief about the client's ability to achieve that goal.

The therapist instructs the client to access his goal again, asking, "Now, as you see yourself sober several months from today, bring to mind that image of your mother. Is there something in that memory that you might use to modify your desired state to make it even more attainable. You mentioned that she was concerned that you might 'give up too soon.' Is there something in that message you need to respond to?"

In this way, the client reviews each of the representations from the original belief for information that might be useful. "If I understand what the message means, it's probably telling me to stick with it a little longer. Like maybe picturing myself more that a few months down the road. I can make an image of myself at my birthday next year still being sober. I think I like that!"

■ STEP 5: IDENTIFY A POSITIVE REFERENCE MODEL

Since we are dealing with clients' beliefs about capabilities here, we need to insure that the new belief we build will work with that specific client. The easiest way is to ask the client to identify a strategy that already works for him and use it as a reference model. For example, the therapist might ask the client to think of something he wants to do in the future that he *knows for certain* he will do or can do. This desired state goal has a built-in positive belief expectancy. As with the irrational belief strategy, the therapist *anchors* this positive resource for future use.

When asked, our example client immediately says, "Oh yes. I'm going to graduate next month. It's been a long time coming, and I really deserve it."

■ STEP 6: STRUCTURAL ANALYSIS

Now that you have a positive strategy as a referent, it is a simple matter of helping the client adjust his desired goal to match this new strategy. This is accomplished by comparing the *structure* of this new goal to the structure of the old goal, and adjusting (using *submodalities*) the original desired goal's visual, auditory, and kinesthetic parts to match the achievable goal's parts.

Again, it is often easiest to start with the visual image. The therapist instructs the client to sit in the appropriate position, eyes up and right, and says, "Now I want you to first bring up that image of yourself graduating. Can you describe how you look?"

Once the description is completed (the therapist uses sub-modalities to ensure a very full description), then the client is instructed to compare that image to his desired goal of sobriety. Where they are different, the therapist instructs the client to alter or shift the *quality* of the image to exactly replicate the quality of the new one.

When the therapist notes some differences, he or she guides the process: "You said the original image of you at your birthday is darker that the image you have of yourself graduating. I want you to adjust the 'brightness' control on the old image so that it is just as bright as the new image. Next, you mentioned that you were looking at yourself graduating from the side. Shift your old image so that you are looking at yourself from the same side and from the same distance." This continues until the images, the tones the words, and feelings match one another.

The net effect of such a procedure is that the client will experience reduced emotional distress when confronted with events that trigger thoughts related to the original belief. This is parallel to the outcome suggested by DeRubeis and Beck (1988) which results from cognitive therapeutic interventions. This is because the cognitive basis for the distress has been attenuated, and the client now has alternative ways of thinking with subsequent changes in his affective state.

So far, we have looked at several disputational techniques and a technique that involves a type of "altered state" with the client. In the next chapter, we will continue to explore various methods for impacting a client's belief systems.

NOTES FOR CHAPTER 6

1. I particularly enjoy Meichenbaum's (1977) definition of this concept. He states, "Cognitive structures seem to be the cognitive psychologist's Rorschach card or 'Linus blanket' – he can see anything he wants to in it and it gives him a sense of security." He goes on to clarify, "By *cognitive structure* I mean to point to that organizing aspect of thinking that seems to monitor and direct the strategy, route, and choice of thoughts" (p. 212-213).

2. See pages 16 to 26 and Appendix A in *Magic of NLP Demystified*. I would also like to thank Carol Martin, a friend and colleague whose work inspired the model.

3. See *Sobriety Demystified: Staying Clean and Sober with NLP and CBT* by this author.

4. Whitehead and Russell, 1910-13 – I have included this citation in the References section of this book, but admit it is not one I have attempted to crack!

5. These patterns are fully detailed in Ellis, et. al. (1988) which cites original work by Ellis as the basis for the models. (see Ellis, 1978/1979)

6. I have drawn many of the example beliefs in this section from Ellis, et. al. (1988).

7. Emotions are complex processes that also include physiology. The "urge" to use will be a combination of emotional feelings combined with physiological changes in body chemistry in response to the "anticipation" of introduction of the chemical (much like Pavlov's dogs salivated in response to the bell, even in the absence of food). In cases where a person is physically dependent, there will also be the physical withdrawal component after a period of deprivation.

8. The term *strategy* differs in RET and NLP. In NLP, the term refers to a sequence or chain of internal events – including visual images, feelings, sounds and words, and taste/smell – that culminate in the accomplishment of some task (thought, feeling, and/or action). This will be described in greater detail in the section on *belief molecules*.

9. The following three strategies are derived from Ellis, et. al., 1988, pps. 28-37.

10. The other two forms of interference are an unwillingness on a "part" of an individual to change and a lack of knowledge of how to change.

11. AVE is a common enough phenomena that it is addressed in several popular self-help guides. In Daley's (1986) workbook, he writes, "You can anticipate feeling guilty and disappointed in yourself after using drugs or alcohol again. But it is important *not to allow these feelings to give you permission to continue using.*" In another relapse prevention workbook, Gorski (1988) plants a very powerful suggestion to counter the "One drink, a drunk" mind set that is often perpetuated by the "old school" of recovery. He writes, "Every addicted person who returns to addictive use will periodically hit moments of sanity during a relapse episode in which they have the power to choose to get help to stop the addictive use" (Manual, p.62).

12. Disputing irrational beliefs is only one of many tools in the RET/RBT therapists' bag of tricks. To describe them all is well beyond the scope of this book. For an exceptionally readable presentation of many of these techniques, I highly recommend the book *Rational-Emotive Therapy with alcoholics and substance abusers* (Ellis, et. al. 1988).

13. Although described in several of his works, his self-help guide *You and your Emotions* (Maultsby and Hendricks, 1974) outlines the process in simple terms that are particularly useful with clients.

14. As noted in Chapter 5, anchoring is an NLP technique borrowed from behavioral psychology. Essentially, it is classical conditioning where the client's internal experience (thought, belief, emotion, vision, etc.) is paired with a touch or gesture (often both). This can then be utilized by the therapist as a "short cut" to assist the client to recall that specific experience.

15. Submodalities are the "fine tuning" aspects of our representations of experience. For example, we might construct an image of ourselves doing something in the future and compare it to a memory of ourselves in the past. The differences will likely be in the sub-modalities of the image. One may be bright and colorful, while the other is darker or dull and in black and white. There is a complete list of sub-modalities in Appendix 3.

16. Pacing and leading represent a particular process in communication. The concept is very well presented in Bandler and Grinder (1975)

IDENTITY
AND
BEYOND

When you change your beliefs

about your identity, it means you are

going to be a different person somehow

(Dilts, et. al., 1990, p. 19).

We are each unique. For all our similarities, there are aspects of us that form the distinction we call *identity*. The sum of my many experiences combined with my physiology form what we generally consider to be the "self." When the therapist begins work at the level of the client's identity, a whole new realm of patterns and strategies come into play. This chapter will discuss interventions that operate on the client's identity.

In reviewing how to present this information, it became clear that there is a division of sorts between the various techniques in terms of their orientation to *time*. Some approaches deal with the clients in the here-and-now, working with specific strategies to change their current actions and emotions. Other techniques look at the client's development over time and focus on specific experiences from the past that have caused suffering or limited growth. Finally, there are several techniques that look forward in time, identifying ways the client can project him or herself into an imagined future in order to identify the capabilities, resources and learnings he or she will need to attain specific desired states.

WORKING IN THE PRESENT

While any work on belief systems will bring to front issues from the client's past, some techniques tend to deal primarily with manifestations of the problem in the present. The underlying assumption is that the client can learn new, more constructive methods of operating without needing to sort through the myriad events that led up to his current position. In this section, we will draw from RET and RBT techniques.

■ TWO COMMON ADDICTIVE BELIEFS

In each of the cases that follow the client expresses a belief about his or her identity. Rather than being about a behavior, a capability, or some other aspect of themselves, the client indicates a reified self-image. Because this image is static and unchanging, it is not alterable and therefore appears "immune" to the typical rational debate. Note, however, how subtle maneuvering by the therapist shifts this nominalized self into a more accessible cognition that can be easily and rationally challenged.

■ I AM A BAD PERSON:

The belief that he or she is inherently "bad" because of an addiction or compulsive disorder is endemic to this population. The ongoing struggle with control, the self-defeating behaviors, the destructive actions addicts finds themselves involved in create intense guilt and shame. This becomes integrated into the innermost concept of the self.[1] It may come out as a generalization: "People who have done the terrible things I've done are *bad* people"; or it may simply be a statement of perceived personal truth: "I'm a terrible, awful, dirty, bad, nasty person because of what I've done." In either case, the focus is on the client's *being* bad.

We see this type of thinking reinforced in young children
when a parent says, "You are a
bad boy," instead of a more appropriate "You did a *bad thing*."
Bad behavior might be an indication of limited resources or
poor judgment, misinformation
or some other problem. It is not
equivalent to *who* a person is.
When confronted with such a
belief, our goal with RET is to
assist the client to accept the
fact that a person can *behave*
badly and not *be* a bad person.

I'M BAD

Using the *distortions* disputational strategy from the last
chapter, the therapist assists the
client to accept this fact. One of
the more finesseful ways to accomplish this is to utilize a series
of Socratic questions to demonstrate that the client already knows this fact. "When a youngster does
something naughty, does that mean he is *bad*, or does
it mean that he made a poor choice and needs correct-
ing?" Then, "How does this relate to your statement
about yourself?" Another dispute is to ask, "If you do
something good for someone, does that make you a *good
person*? How can you be a good person and a bad person at the same time? What does this tell you about the
difference between *how you act* and *who you are*?"
The thrust of the intervention, then, will be to dissociate the client's *actions* from his or her *identity* .

RBT can help the client see how such a belief is counterproductive to recovery by simply using the five
rational questions. In particular, asking the client, "Will
this thinking help protect your health?", and "Will this
thinking help you achieve your short- and long-term
goals?" are two questions that help the client recognize
the cognitive distortions represented by the belief. In
this way, the client will more easily accept the fact that

"I'm a fallible human being who has made mistakes in the past, is likely to make mistakes in the future and is trying to learn from them now."

■ I AM DAMAGED

"I am a worthless drunk." Such a statement conjures up a pitiful image, and this is as true for the listener as it is for the speaker. A person with this belief must battle every moment of every day just to continue living with him or herself. Such a cognitive distortion will need to be successfully challenged before this person can begin recovery. As with the previous example, the goal will be to demonstrate how such thinking not only reflects a distortion of reality but also hampers the client's efforts at recovery.

Inherent in this belief is the idea that because someone has abused alcohol or drugs, they are somehow "damaged". Again we are confronted with a distorted association between behavior and being. Compounding this problem is the client's use of a label. Because a label is a *nominalized* representation of a process (see Chapter 5), it means that, in the mind of the client, the ability to alter this process—to change—is gone. If I am a "worthless alcoholic", then I will always be a worthless alcoholic, *even if I quit drinking*! While it is commonly accepted in the Twelve Step programs that a person remains an "alcoholic" for the rest of his or her life, within that context, this label has a different meaning than what the client above uttered. From the AA perspective, a person is either a "recovering" or a "prac-

I'M DAMAGED

ticing" alcoholic, with no stigma, no judgment, and without the nominalized aspect of our client's label[2].

RBT intervenes with this problem belief by demonstrating to the client how it actively prevents recovery by blocking therapeutic change and growth. Asking, "Will this thinking help you achieve your short- and long-term goals?" and "Will this thinking help you feel the emotions you want to feel?" are two powerful ways to crack this core belief. Once the client can actively question such fundamental qualities of his self-perceptions, the door opens to allow therapeutic inroads in other areas of his or her life.

As soon as the client has successfully challenged this belief, he is encouraged to discard it and replace it with a more realistic and productive belief. This new belief can either be suggested by the therapist or constructed by the client with the therapist's help. My style being somewhat active and directive, I am particularly biased towards the latter. Of course it helps to have in mind an appropriate model towards which we will work. Examples of beliefs to replace the two addictive beliefs above are:

"Doing bad things makes me a person who has *acted* badly but *not* a bad person." This statement reflects the dissociation between identity and actions.

"I am a *recovering* alcoholic. Even if change is slow and difficult, I know it is possible for me." This statement changes the nominalized *alcoholic identity* into a process that implies both personal responsibility and the ability to change.

Once appropriate coping statements have been developed, the client is encouraged to repeat them as often as necessary. They can be written on 3x5 cards and carried in a pocket or on "post-its" and put over a desk or on a mirror. They can be spoken into a tape recorder and played regularly. I strongly urge clients in recovery to establish a regular morning and evening routine. During this time the client can read recovery literature, do Twelve Step and other recovery work, meditate on daily reflections or other inspirational work, and complete REI's developed during counseling sessions. The above coping statements work well when integrated into such meditative activities.

WORKING IN THE PAST

Beliefs tend to fulfill themselves. When you try to argue with a belief in the present, the person is confronting all the data, gathered over time, that supports or "proves" their initial belief. When you go back to where it started, often the issues are much simpler and clearer. They're certainly not cluttered by later confirmations.
Dilts (1990).

Working with dysfunctional belief systems is a challenging approach to treating addictive disorders. Using the following techniques, the therapist impacts the client's belief system at the level of his or her *identity*. As you will see, the provision of new resources or "capabilities" that is the hallmark of the NLP change-history technique covered in the last chapter is integrated into deeper and more elaborate work with belief systems. Again, we turn to the work of Dilts, the primary creator of this technology.

In the previous chapter, we saw how most dysfunctional beliefs are formed as a result of traumatic events. These experiences generally occurred when the client was a more impressionable youngster. The resultant associations are extremely strong and resilient, and are similar in their genesis to what Conrad Lorenz termed "imprints" (Dilts, 1990; Dilts, Hallbom, and Smith, 1990). A good portion of Dilts' work with beliefs involves the freeing up of "rigid" belief systems that result from early traumatic or disturbing imprint experiences. He has taken the philosophical thrust of NLP (i.e., the concepts of *deep structure* and *surface structure* found in the Meta Model and the idea of *limits to the model* found in the *universal human modeling processes*) and applied it to belief systems.

The following NLP technique involves taking the client "back in time" to the influential *imprint experience* that stimulated the formulation of the dysfunctional identity belief. During the session, the client remembers bits and pieces of dialogue from significant people in his or her life at or around the event. There are also visual memories and certain emotions associated with the event. As we saw in the last chapter, these sensory representations of the experience have been incorporated into the belief or belief system.

■ THE IMPRINT EXPERIENCE

We cannot discuss Dilts' work with belief systems without understanding the role of *imprints* in the process. Extrapolating from the early work of Conrad Lorenz, Dilts (1990) defines imprints as specific beliefs that arise from "identity-forming" experiences. His interest in these experiences began after a series of seminars he presented with Timothy Leary, whose goal a number of years ago was to use the LSD experience to change negative or limiting imprints.[3] Dilts and others in the field of NLP have developed drug-free techniques called "re-imprinting" as a means of resolving these dysfunctional patterns of thought[4].

I realized that some traumatic episodes experienced by clients were more than just bad memories that could be dealt with by using simple integration techniques. They were often beliefs and identity forming imprints that formed the cornerstones of a person's personality, and thus required a different approach... Dilts, Hallbom, and Smith, (1990, p. 64)

Because a person's initial imprint experience has the power to influence his everyday thoughts, feelings and actions (without his conscious awareness and even "against his will"!), an intervention that can alter the *structure* of the experience has far-reaching implications on a person's ability to change. The technique that follows has the ring of psychoanalytic approaches wherein the client is assisted in resolving conflicts and problems arising from arrested development at early ages. Of significance, however, is the fact that the work is completed in *one* session rather than over several years of analysis.

Many of our clients come from abusive family backgrounds. Their parents may have loved them and wanted the best for them, but they did not know how to nurture our clients and offer experiences that would promote healthy growth and development. They may have been addicted to alcohol or drugs or to some other mood-altering activity, and this ongoing progressive disorder alienated them from our clients. They may have been emotionally or physically or sexually abusive, trapped in their own world of denial and self-deceit, and our clients were the victims of their disturbance. One of the results of growing up in a dysfunctional family system is that many of our clients carry a "garbage train" of negative past experiences with them into adulthood. This garbage often leads to self-destructive behaviors. A major mechanism in forming these behaviors is the process of imprinting.

IMPRINT EXPERIENCES

When we are very young, we are like "students" in the "school of adulthood". We put on dad's tie and mom's lipstick and imitate the adult behaviors we experience around us. This role-playing occurs *inside* us, unseen, at the cognitive level as well. Eventually, with a great deal of rehearsing, we finally "get it right" and emerge as adults in our own right. We may grow up saying, "I'll *never* be like my parents! I'll never smoke or drink or beat *my* kids!" The problem for many of our clients is, however, this automatic internal rehearsing *imprints* within them the very behaviors they want to avoid. Internalized as deep and complex *core belief systems*, our clients find themselves compelled into behaviors that frustrate and confound them. They are devastated by a sense of powerlessness over this behavior, because there is a sense that it comes from their core: "This is who I am!"

Our clients' early negative imprint experiences may eventually lead them to doing *exactly* what they said they would *never* do, like drinking to excess or beating their own kids. These casualties of dysfunctional family systems are relatively easy to spot. It is the devastating beliefs about one's *self* that often lie hidden. Both of these behaviors are especially amenable to treatment using NLP re-imprinting techniques.

NLP AND DYSFUNCTIONAL BELIEF SYSTEMS

The process developed by Dilts and his colleagues (Dilts, 1990; Dilts, Hallbom, and Smith, 1990) utilizes a number of the techniques we have previously discussed. The intervention can be broken down into three distinct phases: I. Defining the imprint; II. Reframing the intentions; and, III. Building a new experience.

I. DEFINING THE IMPRINT

In the technique that follows, let's examine how a therapist worked with a client who exclaimed in exasperation his belief that "I'm not worth the effort it's going to take to help me get clean and sober!"

■ IDENTIFY THE IMPASSE

The therapist's first step is to identify an "impasse". This is often a point where your client abruptly freezes up, draws a blank, or isn't able to follow you. For example, you've identified a therapeutic goal for the session, but while gathering information, when you ask the client "What stops you from attaining that goal?", the only response you get is, "I don't know."

Gorski (1988) suggests that clients working on relapse prevention issues learn to recognize and work with their impasse experiences in therapy. One of the instructions he provides in completing the *Staying Sober Workbook* is directly related to these emotional "buffers" we install in order to cope with painful experiences. While the client is reading through the 37 "Warning Signs", Gorski writes, "If you find yourself spacing out while reading a warning sign, put a big asterisk next to it. The reason you are spacing out is because your unconscious mind won't let you understand what that warning sign really means." Gorski sees these moments as indicators that a person is unconsciously blocking himself from understanding the warning sign, and that these symptoms should be very carefully scrutinized by the person in recovery.

In our case example, the client identified a belief that was preventing him from moving on with his recovery. A series of statements like, "I don't deserve to get well," and "I'm not worth the time and energy," led the therapist to begin to question him. Using the Meta Model challenges, "You don't deserve it and aren't worth it *according to whom?*" the therapist was met with a blank stare and, "What do you mean? I don't know what you're getting at." The client's physiology (his posture and accessing cues) was one of agitation or anxiety. When asked how he was feeling, he said he felt *angry*, but didn't know at whom or what. "I just feel angry."

It is helpful to anchor the impasse in order to be able to thoroughly explore it using all the systems and submodalities you can. To anchor this type of cognitive experience, the therapist reaches out and grasps the client's arm firmly, establishing a relationship between *that* touch and *that* feeling. In this way, he or she can help the client re-access that feeling later with a "reminding touch".

■ ACCESS THE IMPRINT EXPERIENCE

There are several ways this can be accomplished. One way recommended by Dilts (1990) is to create a "physical time line" upon which the client "walks" back through significant events in his life to the traumatic events that led to the formation of the limiting belief system. Because the experience blocking the person is often made up of a series of self-reinforcing experiences *over time* it can be useful to chart out these events from the present backwards to the original imprint experience.[5] This is accomplished by first having the client access one of the symptoms of the impasse. The easiest symptoms to work with appear to be strong emotions or feelings. In our example, the angry, agitated feeling were a symptom of the impasse. The client accessed those feelings, then walked "back in time", marking each place on the time line where those feelings were prevalent.

Another approach is to assist the client to complete a *transderivational search*[6] using the emotional state as

TIME LINE

the conscious representation from which the client searches through his store of memories with similar associated feelings. This is accomplished by holding the anchor associated with the impasse, and asking the client to bring to mind other experiences where he felt those emotions, then determine the earliest of the experiences[7]. Dilts stresses the importance of being flexible in accepting the client's perceptions as they identify the earliest experience. Memory is not an accurate description of objective reality! As he puts it, "We are not talking about objective reality. We are talking about something much more important: subjective reality, which really determines how you act."

■ IDENTIFY IMPRINT FORMED BELIEFS

As a result of early traumas, the clients make certain generalizations about the world or about themselves and others. These eventually reified into beliefs that coalesce into belief systems that support a negative self-image, a sense of powerlessness, or an inherent distrust or dislike of others. The therapist is now in a position to help the client become consciously aware of these beliefs by asking him or her to verbalize the generalizations that were made at that time.

This requires that the client remain "inside" the remembered traumatic experience, watching what the significant others do, listening to what they say, and attending to how he or she as that younger self responds to the events. The therapist assists the client by asking him or her, "What are you learning from this experience? What generalizations are you making about yourself or other people or about the world?"[8] Then the therapist has the client dissociate from the experience. The easiest way is to have the client "see himself" in the experience as if an objective bystander. From this different perspective, looking back, the therapist asks the client to identify what beliefs he or she formed as a result of the experience?

It is interesting to note that our beliefs may also originate from what we think *others* believe. This comes from our perceptions of their thoughts and judgments based on what we remember them saying, and our interpretations of their behaviors. I want to stress here that this is not objective reality, but rather very subjective. As pointed out above, it is subjective reality that forms the basis for our behaviors.

In our example case, when the client reached his imprint experience (a composite of experiences growing up in a dysfunctional family system—both parents were alcoholics) a central belief resulted from his *perceptions* of what his parents believed. He vividly remembered an incident around his trying to learn how to ride a bicycle. In his memory of the experience, his parents both ridiculed his early attempts, pointing out his clumsiness and awkwardness, and making comments like "I told you you'd fall and hurt yourself," when he would inevitable crash. From their behavior and comments, he deduced that they thought he was a "worthless failure" who would never succeed at anything. This resulted in his feeling angry and impotent and strongly reinforced his negative self image and the beliefs that he "wasn't worth the effort."

I told you you would fall and hurt yourself!

NEGATIVE IMPRINT

II. REFRAMING THE INTENTIONS

In addition to directly challenging the foundation of the client's dysfunctional belief system, this process opens the client to the *possibility* of alternative ways of thinking by using a metaphor: the re-evaluation of other's intentions in the imprint experience. It also initiates the process of building a *meta perspective*—a way of looking at something from outside, having more flexibility and options to evaluate it than are possible from within the experience.

■ DEFINE POSITIVE INTENTIONS

The goal of this step is to challenge the negative perspective the client has habitually held. This is a subtle move that requires finesse and good reframing skills on the part of the therapist. The process begins by having the client imagine he or she is the significant other involved in the imprint experience. If there are more than one, then the process is repeated with each in turn. Once the client is "seeing through the other's eyes", the therapist asks what that person's goal was in doing and saying what they did. Again, there may be a need to reframe into positive statements what the client identifies, especially if he feels anger, remorse, guilt, or fear toward this person. By having the client "become" that person as much as possible, much of the animosity is ameliorated as that person's *positive intentions* become apparent.

In our example, the client became first his father. Observing that his father also held the bike on several occasions, and ran with him for short periods, the client concluded that his father's intention was to "motivate" him to try harder. His mother, on the other hand, was frightened by the danger involved. Her intention was framed as "trying to protect me." Notice how the parent's comments and actions can just as easily accommodate these intentions as the assumed intentions the client fabricated initially.

The next step is to identify the positive intention of the impasse itself. Essentially, the client has created this internal response as a means of "protecting" some important aspect of himself. This step insures the ecological integrity of the system remains intact. From the meta perspective, the therapist asks the client what his or her beliefs associated with the impasse are trying to accomplish that are in the client's best interest. Again, the use of reframing will be important, because, as the client begins to explore these old beliefs, it becomes easier to see just how limiting and pain-producing they have been. The effort in uncovering the positive intention of these beliefs, however, will be rewarded as they help establish criteria for the resources needed in the next step.

III. BUILDING A NEW EXPERIENCE

This process requires the therapist to look at the ecology of the whole system. Remember that beliefs indicate *relationships* between the client's perceptions and memories of people and events. The client's dysfunctional belief *system* resulted in self-destructive or limiting behaviors. However, the integrity of the system needs to remain intact for the re-imprinting process to be successful. Using the following interventions, the therapist alters the *relationships* between the various parts of the client's imprint experience to create a new more constructive experience.

■ PROVIDE NEEDED RESOURCES

There are two parts to this step. We need to help the client first identify what resources he or she needed as a youngster to prevent the formation of the dysfunctional belief system. We also need to help the client identify what resources the significant others in the experience needed in order to accomplish their positive intentio and prevent the negative consequences.

The first step in the process is to assist our clients to identify the resources they needed *at the time of the imprint* that would have enabled them to handle the situation without forming the problematic dys-

CREATING THE RESOURCES

functional belief system. The therapist asks the client to take the dissociated position and, "Look back at that younger you. What did you need then to help you understand and cope with that situation?"

The client's response will be generated at the level of functioning he or she experiences the deficits. Remember earlier we outlined Dilts' hierarchy of the logical levels of human functioning (Chapter 6). The needed resources may come from any one or combination of those levels. They may include beliefs, capabilities, behaviors, or something from the environment. Because the therapist will need to guide the client's formation of these resources, it is important to understand the relationship and possible interactions between these levels.

At the lowest level is the *environment*. Our client may express a desired resource to be a change in the setting: "I needed to not be alone in that alley that afternoon." This environmental resource, however, may require changes in the client's *behavior*: "I wouldn't have been there if I had just told those guys 'No!'" Such a change in behavior may also be dependent on the next higher level of functioning which is the *capability* to both know what you needed to say and the internal resources to say it: "I needed to know how to set appropriate boundaries." But as we previously discussed, capabilities are often dependent upon a person's *beliefs*: "Instead of denial, I needed to firmly believe that it *could* happen to me!" Finally, at the highest level of functioning is the issue of *identity*: "I needed to believe in myself, that I'm smart enough to stay out of those kind of situations."

The therapist helps the client sort to through the levels of functioning to acquire appropriate resources to change the perceptual experience of the imprint situation. As Dilts (1990) says, "Sometimes, even though some people might have the belief and the identity resources already, they just don't have the information. Sometimes people have the information, but they are denying it because they don't have the belief in themselves."

In our case example, the therapist asks, "What did you need as that youngster learning to ride a bicycle that would have helped you feel OK about that experience? What resources did you need to build a different set of beliefs about your parents and your self?" Our client responded with, "It would have helped to believe that my parents loved me and just wanted the best for me." This resource would certainly have provided the client a very different perspective on the situation, one that would have resulted in the fabric of his original belief system being altered significantly.

The next step is to ask the client what resources the significant others needed that would have enabled them to better express their positive intentions previously identified. In our case example, the client responded with "My mom needed to be able to let go and trust me, and my dad needed to be able to tell me I was doing OK in spite of my mistakes." With these internal resources, both parents would have *behaved* differently, altering their *relationship* with their child in his memory of the experience. This internalized relationship of the imprinted parts would have generated an entirely different set of beliefs, empowering rather than effacing the client's self-esteem.

■ INTEGRATE THE NEW RESOURCES

It is one thing to idealize in abstract terms what each of these people needed at that time. It is an entirely different matter to *relive* the experience with these new resources in place. Utilizing the client's ability to fantasize and imagine, we continue the process of building a new experience by having him or her imagine they are each of the people in the experience, one at a time. As the client enters the experience as one of the actors with the new resources available, we ask that he or she re-enact the scene. From the eyes of the younger self, from the body of each of the other people, the therapist asks the client to pay attention to how they feel, what they see and hear, and how others in the situation act. As the scene is played out, the therapist asks what new generalizations can be made and what new beliefs can be built from this revised experience.

In our case example, some of the most profound shifts occurred as he played his father. "I look at my younger self through my father's eyes, and I see him trying so hard. I really want him to succeed. Now that I know that I can just tell him, it's easy. And when I do, the look in his eyes, the pride and sense of accomplishment makes me feel so good. That's exactly what I wanted all along. For my son to feel proud." The therapist worked with the client to create a rich, full and complete representation of each player in the event, drawing from all the representational systems to create as realistic an experience as possible. As the client verbalized the new generalizations and beliefs, we were able to evaluate the success of the process: "Most important to me is that my parents both loved me. They had trouble expressing it, but I know they cared. They were doing the best they could with the resources they had. I don't have to look outside myself for self-worth. I am worth it, because I keep trying in spite of what others say and do. I'm *persistent* if nothing else!"

One aspect of this type of therapeutic is that it addresses the problem of replacing the client's dysfunctional schemata. Rather than simply helping the client to generate a new "core belief" to replace the old, this technique actually builds the new belief into the client's existing cognitive structures by creating new reference experiences. Nothing is left to chance, and the process takes place very rapidly. This means that the therapist can *systematically* assist the client to develop healthier cognitive processes. These processes can in turn oversee the implementation of new beliefs which will prevent continued distortions or other cognitive errors from corrupting the constructive changes.

Dilts (1990) warns us not to attempt to "fool" our clients about the reality of what "really" happened originally, because that memory will always be there. What this technique does, however, is pair the memory of that traumatic experience with it's natural *solution*. Rather than being trapped, afraid, impotent, the client now has other choices of how to think about the experience. This new solution provides an entirely different outcome and a new belief system that the client can now utilize to confront life.

WORKING WITH THE FUTURE

As a final technique, I would like to offer an ingenious method developed by Cameron-Bandler, Gordon, and Lebeau (1985b). This technique again draws upon the client's ability to visualize, fantasize and imagine and incorporates several of the strategies utilized by Dilts in the previous section. The aspect of this method that sets it apart, however, is the way it utilizes present and past perspectives to focus the client on the future. The future, of course, is designed to maximally encourage—to *compel*, in fact—our clients to maximally utilize their resources in the present to their best advantage.

...no one ever took a drink. in order to feel great two weeks from now. ...In fact, reckless, foolish. and indulgent behavior is usually a result. of...NOT generating a compelling future in regard to your potential well-being.
Cameron-Bandler (1986)

Cameron-Bandler (1986) defines compelling future as "...an internally-generated representation of a possible future experience that is responded to as real and ... as possible to attain or avoid if certain actions in the present are taken." Using the following procedure, the therapist helps the client recognize specific strategies that will lead to a desired future and a conscious awareness of behaviors to avoid that would lead to an alternate undesirable future.

What we are talking about here is *goal-directed behavior*. We know when people establish goals, especially long-term goals, the successful ones are going to consistently behave in ways which will most likely take them towards their goal. It is like we have an innate "guidance system" that, once programmed, will continue to mold our behaviors towards achieving that goal. Whenever we vary off the track, the guidance system steps in and corrects our behavior. People who have poorly defined or non-existent goals are more likely to give in to behaviors that will provide immediate gratification without concern for future consequences. These behaviors become habitual, and when combined with mood-altering substances, the addictive process is easily established.

Drawing from observations that people tend to motivate themselves to action using internally-generated images, self-statements, and other cognitive processes, Cameron-Bandler and her colleagues created their treatment procedure to replicate these naturally-occurring processes. In essence, this procedure helps the client *reprogram* his or her internal guidance system towards a more healthy, happy and productive future. The compelling futures process can be divided into three phases: I. Creating a future self-image; II. Completing an inventory; and, III. Painting the future.

I. CREATING A FUTURE SELF–IMAGE

■ CREATE A FUTURE IMAGE

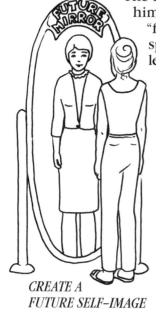

CREATE A FUTURE SELF–IMAGE

The first step requires the client to visualize him or herself as if they were looking at a "future mirror". It is helpful to identify a specific time in the future to focus on, at least several years distant. Five years is a good start, although it could be more or less, depending on the desired goals the client desires. Cameron-Bandler (1986) suggests that it should be at least several years into the future.

■ ASSOCIATE THE FUTURE IMAGE

Once the image is clearly defined—the therapist can utilize sub-modalities to help the client create a full visual representation—the client imagines "stepping into" the image. At this point, the client can see through future eyes, feel the sensations of the future body, hear through those future ears, and taste and smell as they imagine they will at that time. This creates what Dilts (1990) calls a different *perceptual position* from which the client will be able to compare and contrast and generate various cognitive strategies.

After the client has fully experienced that future self, the therapist directs him or her to "step back to the present" and ask that future self, "What do you want from me *now*?" The client is encouraged to verbalize and even write down the response. Because this *imagined* future self will be the result of whatever the client believes he or she will do between now and then to successfully achieve the desired goal, the future self's requests can have significant value in guiding the client towards a more positive future.

STEP INTO
THE FUTURE YOU

II. COMPLETING AN INVENTORY

■ PERSONAL ASSESSMENT 1

In much the same way that the Twelve Step programs require a "searching and fearless moral inventory" (see Chapter 4)[9], the client completes a personal assessment of various areas in his or her life as they are now. This will include both positive and negative perceptions of his or her life, what the client likes and is satisfied with and what he or she dislikes and wants to change. Because addiction profoundly affects all aspects of the client's life, it is important to cover a wide range of areas in this personal assessment. At a minimum, the client may want to list health, relationships, job, finances, accomplishments, and other areas of personal interest or concern.

It is recommended that the client make a written list of these areas and to focus on how they are now, rather than how they "couldawouldashoulda" been. This will give a base-line for comparison with both the past and the desired future.

■ PERSONAL ASSESSMENT 2

Using the same inventory list, the client now goes "back in time" and evaluates each of the same areas as they were five years ago. In both of these exercises and in those that follow, it may be important for the therapist to monitor the client's sense of what is *real*. Everyone creates distortions in their models of the world as we have previously discussed. However, some distortions are so far from center that they may need to be challenged. The therapist can utilize any of the previously covered techniques, such as RBT, RET and Meta Model challenges when confronted with personal evaluations that seem counterproductive. The anorexic client who writes down after *health* for example, "10 pounds overweight", may need an additional intervention before continuing with the exercise!

■ BEHAVIOR LIST – CURRENT CONDITIONS

Now the attention focuses away from the outcome and onto the behaviors that create it. The client is first asked to identify and write down the specific actions or behaviors which created the present conditions. Like the inventory, this will include both positive and negative actions.

This list may also include the full range of levels of human functioning, including environmental influences, behavior, capabilities, and beliefs. In addition, each item listed must be something that is *within the client's power to control*. For example, "being born on the wrong side of the tracks" might be an environmental factor that influenced many of the areas in the client's life; however, that is not something the client has any control over. *Not moving* from that part of town when opportunity arises *is* something the client has control over and would be appropriate to add to the list.

■ BEHAVIOR LIST – WORSE

In this step, the client is asked to fantasize how his or her life could have been worse right now. Then the client is asked what behaviors and actions that were within his or her control would have contributed to that more negative present state. Here the goal is to demonstrate to the client the fact that he or she always exercises choice. It is one of the *convincer strategies* built into this procedure that demonstrates its efficacy to the client. In this case, the client is able to easily see how certain decisions, choices, and actions could have made things worse. This exercise also helps identify behaviors to avoid in the final step of the compelling futures process.

■ BEHAVIOR LIST – BETTER

Again, we are exercising the client's creative abilities as we set the stage for the construction of a compelling future that will best meet the needs of the client. As with the previous steps, the therapist needs to insure the client's responses are realistic and that the behaviors listed are all within his or her control. "Having a million dollars" would make many people's lives better, but it is neither realistic nor within the control of most of our clients.

III. PAINTING THE FUTURE

■ TWO PARALLEL FUTURES

Now the client is instructed to fantasize two parallel futures. One of these will be where he or she *wants* to be in five years, enjoying the fruits of successful and productive behaviors. The other will be a future he or she *doesn't* want to experience, created by continued abuse, denial, unwillingness to change. Each of these futures should include a full visual representation of our clients as they will be in that future, where they live and work, with whom they live and associate, how they feel and act, etc.

■ "THINGS WORTH DOING"

The client is next instructed to access the image of the "desired" future self and ask, "How can I make this happen? What do I need to do to be you?" As the future self responds, the client completes a list of "Things worth doing". This list can include any number of behaviors, but again, all need to be within the direct control of the client. Some may require additional work and planning. "Graduate from school" is something that can help the client achieve the desired future; however, implied within that statement is a great deal of time, effort and energy. Such a goal might be better broken down into component pieces, like, "Develop regular study habits", "Attend all classes", "Ask for help when I need it", etc.

■ "THINGS TO AVOID"

This is a wonderful technique to help the client avoid the pitfalls of "habit" and other behaviors that often reside just outside conscious awareness. By asking the undesirable future self what behaviors are likely to lead to that future, the client will have to examine very closely activities, ways of thinking, attitudes, beliefs, etc. that are likely to lead in the wrong direction. By writing down this "List of things to avoid", the client will have a constant reminder to help guard against falling back on old patterns of thinking and behaving.

The procedure above is a way of generating a self-correcting strategy that will help a client move towards a positive future. The imagined rewards of doing the "things worth doing" and the negative results of slipping into doing "things worth avoiding" create a *compelling future* for the client. This process is an alternate way to create a strategy with our clients that will help them meet the challenges of recovery from addictive disorders. Utilizing our clients' abilities to visualize, to fantasize, to debate with themselves and to learn alternative ways of thinking, all of the interventions presented on the preceding pages can assist in this ongoing process of self-exploration and recovery.

THE ADVENTURE OF RECOVERY

Recovery is an adventure. It is like taking a white water rafting trip. At times things move well, and the client and therapist can sit back and enjoy the scenery, the moods of the river, the smells from the land. At other times, it seems that it is a struggle just to keep their heads above water. Those times can be frightening, but with finesse and flexibility, the therapist can help reframe those moments as "exciting". There are other periods where it is like gliding across serene, quiet reflecting pools. It is during these times that introspection can occur almost effortlessly. The therapist who has at his or her disposal a variety of interventions will be more able to respond to the vast array of presenting problems with which our clients confront us. In addition, having different tools to utilize keeps the process of therapy fresh and exciting for the therapist as well as for the client.

RECOVERY IS AN ADVENTURE

NOTES FOR CHAPTER 7

1. It can be argued that a poor self-image is a precursor to addictive behaviors. We also know that addiction inevitably damages the addict's self-esteem. Rather than argue this point, let's simply agree that it is a common denominator in our addictive population and an issue that will regularly need to be dealt with.

2. Because in AA, the person is either a "recovering alcoholic" or a "practicing alcoholic", there is change or movement involved in the labels. (This comes from the gerund form of the adjective attached to the noun *alcoholic*.) This implies choice, options, hope, etc., where the client's "worthless alcoholic" label is nominalized: there is no hope, because there can be no change. Ever.

3. For those interested in early work on the use of LSD in psychotherapy, I recommend Stanislav Grof's very readable book on the subject called *Realms of the Human Unconscious: Observations from LSD Research*. A significant piece of his work echoes Dilts' concept of belief "molecules" described in the previous chapter. Grof describes a construct he labels *COEX systems* (condensed experiences). These "memory constellations" are what form the basis for a person's "...perception of himself and of the world, his feelings and ideation, and even many somatic processes." p. 49. The bulk of his pioneering work was towards impacting those COEX systems that resulted in psychiatric disorders.

4. Dilts (1990), Dilts, Hallbom and Smith (1990), Cameron-Bandler, Gordon, and Lebeau (1985-a, 1985-b) all utilize re-imprinting techniques as a tool to impact clients' limiting belief systems. It should be noted, however, that Cameron-Bandler, et. al. have developed a technology quite different which they call the emprint method. Emprints are defined as "...an arrangement of steps or procedures which, if followed, will consistently result in the same outcome." (Cameron-Bandler, et. al. 1985b). What these writers present are a series of techniques a person can learn to achieve specific desirable goals. What Dilts and his colleagues present are techniques for altering the beliefs associated with early traumatic identity-forming experiences.

5. Remember, Dilts defines beliefs as *relationships* between perceived aspects of our past experiences. By taking this "journey back in time" we are able to observe how the client has reinforced the dysfunctional belief system throughout his or her life, while eventually recovering the original experience(s) that formed the beliefs to begin with.

6. Bandler and Grinder (1975a) propose that when a person hears or reads something which linguists call the *surface structure*, it results in an unconscious mental search for meaning found in the *deep structure* of verbal communications. This deep structure, however, may vary significantly from the surface structure in the form it takes, and there may be many *derivations* associated with it that are also activated by the search processes. Thus the term *transderivational search* suggests that a person takes a conscious thought or representation of experience (such as a feeling) and unconsciously attempts to attach meaning to it by searching through his stored memories of associated experiences and their derivations.

7. It is important to point out that some imprint experiences may occur suddenly from one traumatic incident, such as a youngster being soundly smacked for disregarding an adult's instructions. I had a client who had an irrational fear of drains; she didn't like washing her hands in the sink and was always uncomfortable while bathing in a tub. When we finally identified the imprint experience, she recounted how she had been beaten by an aunt when she was very young for putting her fingers into the drain of the bathtub after being told not to mess with it. Another type of imprint occurs over time with many experiences reinforcing the belief system. This is often the case with dysfunctional family systems, where a child learns that he or she is "a no good worthless slob" after hearing a drunken parent repeat it over and over many times. In the first case, the client will remember one isolated experience. In the second case, it will likely be a composite of many experiences over time.

8. It can be helpful to prepare the client for this potentially upsetting experience by creating what Dilts calls a "safety sandwich". The therapist asks the client to remember and anchors one pre-imprint experience (before the negative generalizations and beliefs were formed), and one post-imprint experience where the negative beliefs were *not* interfering with the client's life. Should the client become "stuck" in the traumatic memory, the therapist can use these anchored positive experiences to bring him or her out of the memory.

9. In all fairness, we need to consider the amount of time the client has been in treatment before making an analogy between this process and the Fourth Step of AA. As Gorski (1989) observes, clients who are forced into taking the Fourth Step too early are likely only going to complete what he calls a "First Step inventory" (the indicators of unmanageability in their lives). The process we are discussing in this section might often be more appropriately referred to as an "initial inventory"—but we need to be prepared to allow our clients to be as complete in this as they are able and willing to be.

THE ABBREVIATED META MODEL

In *Magic of NLP Demystified* (Lewis & Pucelik, 1982), I attempted to simplify this complex model with a shortened version. I highly recommend those not familiar with this model to read the third chapter in that book on the Meta Model. The illustrations and entertaining style of presentation make it an excellent primer for those not familiar with the original work of Bandler and Grinder. The following is an abbreviated version of the model presented in Chapter 5 of this book. In this case, the model uses examples from various impulse control disorders and presents examples in terms of seven basic Meta Model disputational questions.

■ GATHERING INFORMATION

1. MM Response Question: "Who, what, where, when, how, specifically?"

Use when important information is left out of the client's *surface structure* (deleted) or when it has been unspecified or generalized. The surface structure is the spoken or written part of language. It is what the client says during the session and will indicate, as the examples show, where aspects of the client's model of the world has been deleted, distorted or generalized.

> Example: When the client says, "I'm angry," ask, "Who or what is angering you; How does that make you mad?"

Example: When the client says, "It's like everybody's out to get me," ask, "Who specifically is out to get you?"

2. MM Response Question: "Can you say that about yourself?"

Use when the client says something about another person that probably applies to himself.

Example: When the client says: "She never seems to understand me," say, "Can you say, 'I never seem to understand her'?"

Example: When the client says, "My boss hates me," say, "What do you experience when you say, 'I hate my boss'?"

■ EXPANDING LIMITS

3. MM Response Question: "What stops you? What would happen if you did?"

Use when you hear words like "can't", "should" or "must" to uncover the client's catastrophic expectations.

Example: When the client says, "I can't quit," ask, "What stops you from quitting?"

Example: When the client says, "I must be understanding," ask, "What would happen if you weren't?"

4. MM Response Question: "Can you think of a time (situation) when you did (didn't)?"

Use when the client indicates the belief that there are *no* exceptions.

Example: When the client says, "Everyone thinks I'm crazy," ask, "Can you tell me one person who doesn't? You mean *everyone* thinks you're crazy, even your pet rock?"

Example: When the client says, I always drink when I'm angry," ask, "Think of a time when you were angry and didn't drink?"

■ CHANGING MEANINGS

5. MM Response Question: "How do you know?"

Use when the client is mind reading.

> Example: When the client says, "I know he thinks I'm still using," ask, "How do you know?"

> Example: When the client says, "They know I'm trying," ask, "How do they know?"

6. MM Response Question: "How do they (you) make you (them) feel that way?"

Use when the client expresses cause-effect relationships with other's emotions.

> Example: When the client says, "She makes me want to get loaded," ask "How does she *make* you want anything?"

> Example: When the client says, "I feel guilty for making her unhappy," ask, "How does what you do make her feel emotions?"

7. MM Response Question: "According to whom?"

Use when you hear an unsubstantiated value judgement.

> Example: When the client says, "It's not good to get your hopes up," ask, "Not good according to whom?"

> Example: When the client says, "He's not working a good program ," ask, "Who believes that he is not working a good program?"

As the above examples demonstrate, the structure of the client's language is both revealing and functional. By systematically challenging the client's beliefs as represented in his or her language, the therapist can significantly impact the health of the client's model of the world.

NLP ACCESSING CUES

In order to fully appreciate the NLP techniques presented in this volume, it is important to understand the role of accessing cues in the process. Accessing cues are the minute behavioral signals called *minimal cues* the client gives out that indicate specific ways of thinking. Because the structure of a thought is often just as, if not more important as the content of the thought, these cues help the therapist fine tune the work in progress.

What follows is a partial list and examples of the various accessing cues referred to in the text. For more information, the reader is referred to the texts at the end of this appendix.

The most well known and easily observed of the accessing cues are the client's eye movements. Each move is an indication of a different type of cognitive process:

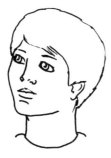
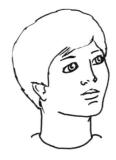

VISUAL CONSTRUCTED
UP RIGHT

VISUAL REMEMBERED
UP LEFT

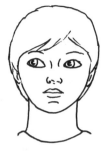 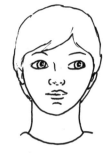

CONSTRUCTING SPEECH   **REMEMBERING SOUNDS**
LEVEL RIGHT   **LEVEL LEFT**

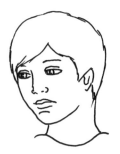 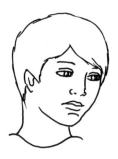

ACCESSING FEELINGS   **INTERNAL DIALOGUE**
DOWN RIGHT   **DOWN LEFT**

Another source of information about what type of activity is occurring in the client's brain is from postural indicators and breathing patterns.

VISUAL POSTURE
Straight, erect,
head and
shoulders up.
Breathing high
in chest.

KINESTHETIC POSTURE
Curved, bowed,
head and
shoulders down.
Breathing low
into abdomen.

AUDITORY POSTURE

Upright,
"telephone" posture,
head tilted to side.
Breathing full range.

*DIGITALIZED POSTURE

Erect,
head up and
arms folded.
Breathing restricted.

Still another indicator of how the client is processing information comes from qualities of voice, including tone, volume, and speed.

VISUAL ACCESSING

High, clear,
loud and fast.

KINESTHETIC ACCESSING

Low, airy,
soft and slow.

AUDITORY ACCESSING

Melodic,
variable, rhythmic.

*DIGITAL ACCESSING

Monotonic,
consistent, clipped.

Finally, there are words which presuppose one or another of the sensory systems. Called *predicates*, these words tell the listener what type of process the client is using to understand and communicate.

VISUAL PREDICATES

Look it over,
I see what you're saying,
That's a colorful expression.

KINESTHETIC PREDICATES

Get a feel for it,
I've got a handle on it,
That's a warm expression.

AUDITORY PREDICATES

Sound them out,
I hear what you're saying.
That expression rings true.

*DIGITAL PREDICATES

Reason it out,
I understand what you're saying.
That expression makes sense.

*The digital system describes someone who is using something other than a sensory-based representation (seeing, feeling, hearing, tasting, or smelling). While the term originates in computer technology, where information is stored in "digital bits", rather than in an analog format, it aptly describes the processes whereby thinking does not directly presuppose one of our sensory systems.

■ SUGGESTED FURTHER READING:

One of the cleanest descriptions of minimal cues can be found in Lewis and Pucelik (1982) *Magic of NLP Demystified: A Pragmatic Guide to Communication and Change*. Descriptions of accessing cues and representational systems can also be found in almost every book written on NLP.

SUB-MODALITIES

The following is a partial list of submodalities by representational system. The more you work with representational systems, the more important the submodalities become. Especially important are the fine-tuning work done with belief system changes. The following list is derived from Gordon (1978):

VISUAL	KINESTHETIC	AUDITORY	OLFACTORY
color	temperature	pitch	fragrance
brightness	pressure	loudness	concentration
saturation	texture	timbre	essence
shape	form	pattern	texture
location	location	location	location

One of the early masters of the art of submodalities, Richard Bandler (1985) incorporates these distinctions into his "Swish" technique. By building two distinct images of oneself in the present state and in the desired state, then manipulating these images using submodalities, Bandler helps the client generate an alternative choice. This is similar to the compelling future technique discussed in Chapter 7. Especially helpful is the list of visual submodality distinctions he has developed for his work. I highly recommend his book for the counselor looking to expand upon and fine-tune a client's mental imagery. These skills can greatly facilitate some of the techniques covered in Chapters 6 and 7.

RESOURCES

A.A. World Services, Inc., Box 459, Grand Central Station, New York, NY 10163. You can obtain the "Big Book" and the "Twelve and Twelve" from them as well as other AA literature and materials.

Hazelden Educational Materials, Box 176, Center City, MN 55012, (800) 328-9000 U.S, except in Minnesota. Send for their catalog—they have the most complete selection of recovery books, pamphlets and other odds and ends in the world.

The CENAPS Corporation and Herald House/Independence Press, P.O. Box HH, 3225 South Noland Road, Independence MO 64055, (800) 767-8181. CENAPS offers all of Terrance Gorski and Merlene Miller's works on Relapse Prevention. They also offer workshops and trainings.

FuturePace Inc., P.O. Box 1173, San Rafael, CA 94915, (408) 485-1200, Leslie Cameron-Bandler, one of the originators of NLP also offers trainings and consultation along with her colleagues.

Metamorphous Press, P.O. Box 10616, Portland, OR 97210, These folks have a great selection of NLP materials and other self-help and professional titles.

The NLP University, P.O. Box 1112,Ben Lomond, CA 95005, (408) 336-3457 or FAX (408) 336-5854. Designed several years ago by Robert Dilts and Tod Epstein, the NLP University offers an intensive summer program in applications of NLP.

The VAK is a quarterly newsletter on NLP and can be obtained from: 240A Twin Dolphin Drive, Redwood City, CA 94065, (415) 595-7795, (800) 228-4069

Rational Self Help Books, Division of R.S.A. Inc., 2036 Blairmore Road, Lexington, KY 40502. You can order RBT materials from them.

Another address is: Rational Behavior Therapy books, tapes and other materials. Dr. Maxie Maultsby, Jr., **RSA, Inc.**, P.O. Box 22146, Lexington, KY 40522. Maultsby has a wonderfully useful audio cassette and bibliotherapy booklet training program, *The Professional's Self-Training Kit for Group RBT*. This extremely useful program is one of the best ways to learn RBT that I have seen and is available through RSA, Inc.

Rational Recovery, (Jack Trimpey's alternative to Twelve Step Programs). For national information, call (916) 621-4374 or 621-2667.

The Journal of Rational Recovery* and *Rational Revcovery from Alcoholism: The Small Book, 3rd Ed. can be obtained from Lotus Press, Box 800, Lotus, CA 95651.

REFERENCES

____*Alcoholics anonymous* (3rd Ed., 1976), New York, NY: Alcoholics Anonymous World Services, Inc.

____*Twelve steps and twelve traditions*, (33rd printing, 1986), New York, NY: Alcoholics Anonymous World Services, Inc.

American Psychiatric Association (1994). *Diagnostic and statistical manual of mental disorders* (4th Ed.), Washington, D.C.: American Psychiatric Association.

Bandler, R. (1985). *Using your brain—for a change*, Ed. by C. Andreas & S. Andreas. Moab, UT: Real People Press.

Bandler, R. & Grinder, J. (1979). *Frogs into princes*, Moab, Utah: Real People Press.

Bandler, R. & Grinder, J. (1975a). *Patterns of the hypnotic techniques of Milton H. Erickson, M.D. (Vol. I)*, Cupertino, CA: Meta Publications.

Bandler, R. & Grinder, J. (1975b). *The structure of magic, Volume I*, Palo Alto, CA: Science and Behavior Books, Inc.

Bandler, R. & Grinder, J. (1982). *Reframing*, Moab, Utah: Real People Press.

Bandura, A. (1965). Vicarious processes: A case of no-trial learning. In L. Berkowitz (Ed.), *Advances in experimental social psychology, (Vol 2)*, New York: Academic Press.

Bandura, A. (1977). *Social learning theory*, Englewood Cliffs, NJ: Prentice Hall.

Bateson, G. (1971). The cybernetics of "self": A theory of alcoholism. *Psychiatry*, 34:1, pp. 1-18.

Bateson, G. (1972). *Steps to an ecology of mind*, New York, NY: Ballantine Books.

Beattie, M. (1986) *Denial*, Center City, MD: Hazelden Foundation.

Beebe, J. P. (1990). *The codependent counselor: Guidelines for Self-assessment and change*, Independence, MO: Herald House/Independence Press.

Brownell, & Marlatt, A. (1986). Understanding and preventing relapse. *American psychologist*, (41) 765-782.

Blum, K. & Payne, J.E. (1991). *Alcohol and the addictive brain: New hope for alcoholics from biogenetic research*, New York, NY: The Free Press; a division of Macmillan, Inc.

Cameron-Bandler, L. (1986). Influencing behavior in the alcoholic family: Strategies for creating a compelling future. *Focus on family and chemical dependency*, Vol 9 #4, July/Aug 1986. pp 6-44.

Cameron-Bandler, L., Gordon, D., & Lebeau, M. (1985a). *The emprint method: A guide to reproducing competence*, San Rafael, CA: FuturePace, Inc.

Cameron-Bandler, L., Gordon, D., & Lebeau, M. (1985b). *Know how: Guided programs for inventing your own best future*, San Rafael, CA: FuturePace, Inc.

Daley, D. C. (1986). *Relapse prevention workbook for recovering alcoholics and drug dependent persons*, Holmes Beach, FL: Learning Publications, Inc.

Darling, M. (1988). A second look at NLP. *Training*, January: 38-42.

DeRubeis, Robert J. & Beck, Aaron T. (1988). Cognitive therapy. In K. Dobson (Ed.), *Handbook of cognitive-behavioral therapies*, New York, NY: The Guilford Press.

Dilts, R. (1990). *Changing belief systems with NLP*, Cupertino, CA: Meta Publications.

Dilts, R., Grinder, J., Bandler, R., Cameron-Bandler, L., & De Lozier, J. (1980) *Neuro-linguistic programming volume I: The study of the structure of subjective experience*, Cupertino, CA: Meta Publications.

Dilts, R., Hallbom, T., & Smith, S. (1990). *Beliefs: Pathways to health and well-being*, Portland, OR: Metamorphous Press.

Dobson, K., & Block, L. (1988). Historical and philosophical bases of the cognitive-behavioral therapies. In K. S. Dobson (Ed), *Handbook of cognitive-behavioral therapies*, New York, NY: The Guilford Press.

Donovan, D. M. (1988). Assessment of addictive behaviors: Implications of an emerging biopsychosocial model. In D. M. Donovan & G. A. Marlatt (Eds), *Assessment of addictive behaviors*, New York, NY: Guilford Press.

Donovan, D. M. & Chaney, E. F. (1985). Alcoholic relapse prevention and intervention: Models and methods. In G. A. Marlatt & J. R. Gordon (Eds.), *Relapse prevention: Maintenance strategies in the treatment of addictive behaviors*, New York, NY: The Guilford Press.

Ellis, A. (1978-1979). Discomfort anxiety: A new cognitive behavioral construct. Parts I and II. *Rational Living, 14*(2), 3-8; *15*(1), 25-30.

Ellis, A. (1989). The history of cognition in psychotherapy. In A. Freeman, K. M. Simon, L. E. Beutler, & H. Arkowitz (Eds.), *Comprehensive handbook of cognitive therapy*, New York, NY: Plenum Press.

Ellis, A. & Dryden, W. (1987). *The Practice of Rational Emotive Therapy*, New York, NY: Springer Publishing Company.

Ellis, A., McInerney, J. F., DiGiuseppe, R., & Yeager, R. J. (1988). *Rational emotive therapy with alcoholics and substance abusers*, New York, NY: Pergamon Press.

Fingarette, H. (1988). *Heavy drinking: The myth of alcoholism as a disease*, Berkeley and Los Angeles, CA: University of California Press.

Freeman, A., Pretzer, J., Fleming, B., & Simon, K. (1990). *Clinical applications of cognitive therapy*, New York, NY: Plenum Press.

General Services Office of Alcoholics Anonymous (1988). Analysis of the 1983 survey of the membership of A.A. In *Fact File*, New York, NY: A.A. Publishing.

Goldfried, M. R. (1989). Foreword. In A. Freeman, K. M. Simon, L. E. Beutler, & H. Arkowitz (Eds.), *Comprehensive handbook of cognitive therapy*, New York, NY: Plenum Press.

Gordon, D. (1978). *Therapeutic metaphors*, Cupertino, CA: Meta Publications.

Gorski, T. T. (1988). *The staying sober workbook instruction manual*, Independence, MO: Independence Press.

Gorski, T. T. (1989). *Understanding the twelve steps: A guide to counselors, therapists, and recovering people*, Independence, MO: Herald House/Independence Press.

Gorski, T. T., & Miller, M. (1982). *Counseling for relapse prevention*, Independence, MO: Herald House/ Independence Press.

Gorski. T. T., & Miller, M. (1986). *Staying sober: A guide for relapse prevention*, Independence, MO: Independence Press.

Grinder, J., & Bandler, R. (1976). *The structure of magic, Vol II*, Palo Alto, CA: Science and Behavior Books.

Grinder, J. & Bandler, R. (1981). *Trans-formations*, Moab, Utah: Real People Press.

Griffin-Shelley, E. (1990) *Maintaining sobriety with bibliotherapy*, (pamphlet), Center City, MN: Hazelden Educational Materials.

Jacobson, G. R. (1989). A comprehensive approach to pretreatment evaluation: I. Detection, assessment, and diagnosis of alcoholism. In R. K. Hester & W. R. Miller (Eds), *Handbook of alcoholism treatment approaches*, New York, NY: Pergamon Press.

Jaffe, J. H. (1980). Drug addiction and drug abuse. In A. G. Gilman, L. S. Goodman, & A. Gilman (Eds.), *The pharmacological basis of therapeutics* (6th Ed.), New York, NY: MacMillan Publishing Co.

Jampolski, L. (1991). *Healing the addictive mind*, Berkeley, CA: Celestial Arts.

Jellinek, E. M. (1952). The phases of alcohol addiction. *Quarterly Journal of Studies on Alcohol, 13,* 673-684.

Jellinek, E. M. (1960). *The disease concept of alcoholism*, New Brunswick, NJ: Hillhouse Press.

Johnson, V. E. (1980). *I'll quit tomorrow* (Rev. Ed.). New York, NY: Harper and Row.

Katz, S. J., & Liu, A. E. (1991). *Codependency conspiracy: How to break the recovery habit and take charge of your life*, New York, NY: Warner Books, Inc.

Kazdin, A. E. (1978). *History of behavior modification; experimental foundations of contemporary research*, MD: University Park Press.

Keller, M. (1972). On the loss of control phenomenon in alcoholism. *British journal of addiction*, 67: 153-166.

Khantzian, E. J., Halliday, K. S., & McAuliffe, W. E. (1990). *Addiction and the vulnerable self: Modified dynamic group therapy for substance abusers*, New York, NY: The Guilford Press.

Lewis, B., & Pucelik R. F. (1982). *Magic of NLP demystified: A pragmatic guide to communication and change*, Lake Oswego, OR: Metamorphous Press.

Ludwig, A. M., Wikler, A., & Stark, L. H. (1974). The first drink: Psychobiological aspects of craving. *Archives of General Psychiatry, 30,* 539-547.

Mahoney, M. J., & Arnkoff, D. B. (1978). Cognitive and self-control therapies. In S. L. Garfield & A. E. Bergen (Eds.), *Handbook of psychotherapy and behavior change: An empirical analysis*, New York, NY: Wiley.

Marlatt, G. A. (1985). Relapse Prevention: Theoretical Rationale and Overview of the Model. In G. A. Marlatt

& J. R. Gordon (Eds.) *Relapse prevention: Maintenance strategies in the treatment of addictive behaviors*, New York, NY: The Guilford Press.

Martin, J. C. (1989). *Chalk talks on alcohol*, San Francisco, CA: Harper and Row Paperback Edition. This work was originally published under the title *No Laughing Matter*, drawn in part from the U.S. Navy film, "Chalk Talk on Alcohol," made in 1972.

Maultsby, M. C. (1975). *Help yourself to happiness through rational self-counseling*, New York, NY: Institute for Rational-Emotive Therapy.

Maultsby, M. C. (1981). *The professional self-training kit for group RBT*, Lexington, KY: R.S.A. Inc.

Maultsby, M. C. (1978). *The rational behavioral alcoholic-relapse prevention treatment method*, Lexington, KY: Rational Self-Help Aids, Inc.

Maultsby, M. C. (1984). *Rational behavior therapy*, Englewood Cliffs, NJ: Prentice-Hall, Inc.

Maultsby, M. C., & Hendricks, A. (1974). *You and Your Emotions*, Lexington, KY: Rational Self-Help Books, R.S.A. Inc.

Meichenbaum, D. (1977). *Cognitive-behavior modification*, New York, NY: Plenum Press.

McClendon, T. (1989). *The wild days: NLP 1972 - 1981*, Cupertino, CA: Meta Publications.

Miller, M. (1989). *Recovery education: A guide for teaching chemically dependent people*, Independence, MO: Herald House/Independence Press.

Miller, N. (1974). Applications of learning and biofeedback to psychiatry and medicine. In A. Freedman, H. Kaplan, & B. Sadock (Eds.), *Comprehensive textbook of psychiatry*, Baltimore: Williams & Wilkins.

Miller, W. R. (1989). Increasing motivation for change. In R. K. Hester & W. R. Miller (Eds.), *Handbook of alcoholism treatment approaches*, New York, NY: Pergamon Press.

Miller, W. R., & Hester, R. K. (1980). Treating the problem drinker: Modern approaches. In R. W. Miller (Ed.), *The addictive behaviors: Treatment of alcoholism, drug abuse, smoking, and obesity*, Oxford, England: Pergamon Press.

Miller, W. R., & Hester, R. K. (1989). Treating alcohol problems: Toward an informed eclecticism. In R. K. Hester & W. R. Miller (Eds), *Handbook of alcoholism treatment approaches*, Elmsford, NY: Pergamon Press.

____*Narcotics anonymous* (1982), New York, NY: C.A.R.E.N.A. Publishing Co.

Nathan, P.E. (1980). Etiology and process in the addictive behaviors. In W.R. Miller (Ed.), The addictive beh*aviors: Treatment of alcoholism, drug abuse, smoking, and obesity*, Elmsford, NY: Pergamon Press.

Nordby, V. J., & Hall, C. S. (1974). *A guide to psychologists and their concepts*, San Francisco, CA: W. H. Freeman and Company.

Pearsons, J. (1989). *Cognitive therapy in practice: A case formulation approach*, New York, NY: W.W. Norton & Company.

Perls, F. (1973). *The gestalt approach and eye witness to therapy*, Palo Alto, CA: Science and Behavior Books.

Prochaska, J. O., & DiClemente, C. C. (1982). Transtheoretical therapy: Toward a more integrative model of change. *Psychotherapy: Theory, Research, and Practice*, 19; 276-288.

Robertson, N. (1988). *Getting better, inside alcoholics anonymous*, New York, NY: William Morrow & Co., Inc.

Rogers, R., & McMillin, C. S. (1989). *Don't help: A guide to working with the alcoholic*, New York, NY: Bantam Books.

Sikorsky, I. I. (1990). *AA's godparents: Three early influences on alcoholics anonymous and its foundation*, Minneapolis, MN: CompCare Publishers.

Smith, D. E., & Wesson, D. R. (1988). Cocaine abuse and treatment: An overview. In *Treating cocaine dependency*, Center City, MO: Hazelden Educational Materials.

Stamas, D. (1981). Breaking through the family's denial. In *Alcoholism, a family matter*, Pompano Beach, FL: Health Communications, Inc.

Swift, H. (1984). *A.A. and bibliotherapy*, Center City, MN: Hazelden Educational Materials.

Trimpy, J. (1986). *Rational recovery from alcoholism: The small book*, Lotus, CA: Lotus Press.

Vaillant, G. E. (1983). *The natural history of alcoholism: Causes, patterns, and paths to recovery*, Cambridge, MA: Harvard University Press.

Vuchinich, R. E., Tucker, J. A., & Harlee, L. M. (1988). Behavioral assessment. In D. M. Donovan & G. A. Marlatt (Eds,) *Assessment of addictive behaviors*, New York, NY: The Guilford Press.

Voegtlin, W., & Lemere, F. (1942). The treatment of alcohol addiction, *Quarterly journal on studies of alcoholism*, 2:717.

Washington, A. M. (1989) *Cocaine addiction: Treatment, recovery, and relapse prevention*, New York, NY: W. W. Norton & Company.

Whitehead, A. N. & Russell, B. (1910-13). *Principia Mathematica* (3 Vols., 2nd Ed), Cambridge, Cambridge University Press.

Wolpe, J. (1969). *The practice of behavior therapy*, New York: Pergamon Press.

INDEX

A

abstinence anxiety **152**, 153, 154, 155, 157, 158, 162
abstinence violation effect (AVE) 160
accessing cues 9, 166, 188, **211**, 215
addiction, models of 17-35, defined 38-44
Al-Anon 71
alcohol and other drug abuse 40-44
alcoholic personality 24
Alcoholics Anonymous (AA) **22-24**, 70-82
alcoholism 16, 17, multiple alcoholisms 39
American Disease Model **21**, 23, 51, 76, 113
anchor, anchoring, 33, 120, **145**, 169, 174, 177, 188, 190, 205, 206
anonymity 72
antabuse 26, 42
automatic thoughts 117, 123, 134, 149, 153
AVE *see* abstinence violation effect
aversion therapy 26

B

behaviorism 11, **26**
    behavior modification 11
    behavior therapy 5, 11, 12
beliefs 147-149
belief molecule **167**, 170, 176
belief system **30**, 85, 88, 92, 150, 180, 184, 187, 189, 190, 193, 195,
biopsychosocial model 31, 35, **39**
black box 169
blackout 21

C

catastrophizing 133, 134
cause and effect **130**, 133, 134
classical conditioning 26, 145, 177
Cocaine Anonymous 22, 74
cognitive disputations 123
cognitive distortions **123**, 124, 131, 139, 146
cognitive errors **131**, 135, 136, 146
cognitive-behavioral therapy *defined* 2-3
cognitive-restructuring 9
collaborative empiricism 120
comparing out 132

compelling future **197**, 198, 202
constraints *on our models of the world* 148
constructive alternativism 34
controlled drinking 50, 51, **52**, 67
convincer strategies 201
coping-skills therapy 9, 10
core belief system **30**, 187
core cognitions 151
course specifiers 42
craving 23, 27, **33**, 45, 47

D

deep structure **83**, 86, 184, 205
defects of character 70, 95, 97
deletion 9, 47, **124**, 131
demandingness **137**, 138
denial 46-50, 56, 57, 59, 61, 63, 68, 69, 84, 85, 90, 95, 99, 125,
        134, 186, 194, 201
depersonalizing 136
dichotomous thinking **131**, 140
direct amends 70, 100
discomfort anxiety **151**, 152, 158
discriminatory functions 28, 33
disputational technique 123, **136**
disqualifying the positive 133
dissociated state therapy 10
distortion 9, 30, 47, **124**, 131, 181, 196, 200
disulfiram *(see antabuse)*
drunkologue 23

E

ecological check 96, **163**
emergent *model* 35, *paradigm* 15, 19, 39, *view* 19
euphoric recall 69
exaggerating 136, 137

F

feedback loop 33, 173
fellowship 24, 75, 76, **77**, 83, 90, 102, 106, 107, 108, 111, 113
five rational questions 181
fortune telling 133
4-tuple 47
future pacing 136, 164

G

generalization 9, 32, 47, **124**, 128, 131, 148, 167, 180, 190, 195,
        196, 205

genetic marker 60
genetic model 27
Gestalt 7, 13

H

Higher Power (HP) 79, **87**, 88, 89, 92, 93, 103, 104, 105, 110, 114
hit bottom 21, 22
holistic doctrine 7

I

impasse **187**, 188, 189, 190, 192
imprint 184, **185**, 186, 187, 189, 190, 191, 193, 194, 195, 204, 205
informed eclecticism 34
internal dialogue **11**, 12, 212
interventions xv, xvi, 23, 26, 30, 32, 34
irrational strategies 151
Isomorphism 7, **13**

L

labeling 92, **135**, 160, 167
leading *(see pacing and leading)*
lifestyle change 64
linguistic presupposition 86
locus of control 99
logical levels of change 89
lost performative 130
low frustration tolerance (LFT) 152, **153**, 154

M

make amends 70, 82, 98, 106
making positive affirmations 137
map (maps, mapping) 9, **12**, 47, 119, 145
mediational effect 3, 6
medical model *(see also American Disease Model)* 50, 51, 110
meta model 123, **124**, 132, 133, 134, 137, 141, 146, 167, 184, 188, 200
meta part 88, 104
meta perspective 191, 192
mind reading **128**, 133, 167, 209
minimal cues 9, 166, 169, **211**, 215
modal operator *(of necessity)* 127, 135, *(of possibility)* **127**, 128, 140
Modified Dynamic Group Therapy (MDGT) 24
moral inventory 70, 82, **91**

N

Narcotics Anonymous 74, 113, 114
neuro-linguistic programming *defined* 2-3
nominalizations 126

O

obsessive drugs 41, 53
operant conditioning 26
overgeneralizations 132
Oxford Group 22, 75, 81, 113, 114

P

pacing and leading 121, **145**, 172, 177
personalization 135
polarized role playing 137
polydrug abuse 53
positive expectancies 29
positive intention **192**, 193, 195
post acute withdrawal 32
predicates 119
primary disease 20, 22
problem-solving therapies 9, 10
prohibition 20, 22
psychoanalysis 24
psychobiological model 33
psychogenetic theory 27
psychotherapy 12, 204

R

rapport 118, **119**, 120, 123
reality therapy 15
referential index *deleted* 125, *generalized* 128, *reversed* 126,
    unspecified 125
reframing **136**, 187, 191, 192
reinforcing attributes 26
relapse xvi, 16, 19, 22, 31, 41, 55, 56, 57, 64, **65**, 68, 69, 79, 160,
    177, 188
relapse prevention xvi, 149, 177, 188
representational systems 8, **12**, 47, 119, 145, 170, 196, 215, 217
requisite variety 18

S

schemata 3, 12, 30, **147**, 148, 196
secondary gains 96
serenity prayer 90, 114

shame 55, 100, 159, 160, **180**
"should" statements 134
six-step reframing 10, 96
social diagnosis 40, 41
social learning theory 28, 33, 36
spiritual awakening 70, 75, **78**, 80, 81, 90, 94, 105
sponsor 18, 77, **78**, 87, 90, 94, 95, 96, 101, 102
stage model of motivation 59-64, 85, 88, 90, 97, 98, 101
submodalities 174, 177, 188, **217**
surface structure 83, 86, **207**
surrender xv, 82, 84, 111, 114
synesthesia 170

T

temperance 75, 77
Theory of Logical Types 150
therapeutic environment 118
TIQ 27, 28
tolerance 21, 26, 38, 41, 42, 52
transderivational search 189, **205**
twelve step meetings 73, *open meeting* 73, *speakers meeting* 61, 74
twelve-stepping 78

U

underlying assumptions 131
universal human modeling processes 9, 47, 124, 131, 184
universal quantifiers 128
unspecified verbs 127

V

visualizing 137, 170

W

well-formed outcome 121, 122
withdrawal 21, 32, 33, 38, 40, 41, 42, 52, 57, 75, 154, 176

Kelsey & Co.
Publishing

Kelsey & Co. is a new publisher. Our emphasis is on works representing the state-of-the-art in neuro-linguistic programming, cognitive-behavioral therapy, transpersonal psychology, hypnosis, and addiction counseling and recovery. We are dedicated to bringing innovative and "user-friendly" information on therapeutic techniques and self-directed recovery to the public. Our Professional Counselor series is designed to fit the needs for continued growth of psychologists, counselors and other professional people helpers. Kelsey & Co. takes a special interest in new and unpublished authors with innovative and creative ideas.

The following pages contain descriptions of upcoming works. We invite your comments and suggestions.

Upcoming Works

Professional Counselor Handbooks

Volume II	**Sobriety Demystified:** *Staying Clean and Sober with NLP and CBT*

by Byron A. Lewis

Emphasizing self-directed patterns of change, ***Staying Clean and Sober*** provides the counselor with tools to support the process of recovery using approaches from Nuero-Linguistic Programming and Cognitive Behavioral Therapies. As in his other books, Byron takes very complex concepts and techniques and makes them simple and easy to use. Peppered with entertaining and informative illustrations by Leslie Lewis, this volume is a must for anyone working in the field of addictive disorders.

Volume III	**Recovering Ritual and Ceremony:** *Applications of Transpersonal Psychology to Addiction Treatment*

by Bruce Campbell

Bruce presents remarkable insights into the recovery process from the perspective of transpersonal psychology. He whisks the reader away on a journey through a richly textured fabric of theory, beliefs, and practices. From a historical perspective, he reviews the ritual and ceremonial dimension of the human experience. During this process, the reader rediscovers the ancient and spiritual roots of recovery. Bruce believes that this spiritual foundation of the recovery process has been displaced in contemporary approaches to treatment and offers a comprehensive model which reaffirms the spiritual experience as the core to successful prevention and treatment.

**Volume
IV**

Reality Wars:
Dissociated State Therapy

*by A. John McBee and
R. Frank Pucelik*

This book represents a tremendous leap forward in understanding human behavior. The genius of these authors is in making a dynamic and complex approach to therapy come alive. One of the things which makes this book unique is the presentation of the specific models that came out of the original NLP Human Modeling research. Plenty of examples, easy to follow steps and "programmed instruction" exercises guide the reader to a full understanding of the process.

❖ ❖ ❖

Other New Works

Hypnotherapy Handbook:
A Guide to Client-Centered Hypnosis

by Margie Way

Margie writes: "Client-centered hypnotherapy is a method by which a hypnotherapist provides a safe place for the client's creative subconscious to quietly and lovingly stop and take a look at what is really going on." Blending the best from NLP, Ericksonian hypnosis and other disciplines, Margie leads the reader through topics such as self-care, developing your trance voice, anchoring, defining the problem/solution, telephone intakes, reframing and a host of other pragmatic tools. A combination textbook/workbook/journal, this work is the ideal companion for any student of hypnosis.

A Chink in the Armor:
Assessment/Intervention Group Processes

by James Ronan, Jr.
and Byron Lewis

In the mid-1980's James Ronan, Jr. and Byron Lewis developed a highly effective approach to the initial treatment of substance-abusing individuals. This long-awaited version of their program comes in notebook format with reproducible worksheets, plans for a flip chart, and other useful tools. Ideal for treatment and school programs, drug-court and first offender programs, etc., this volume also includes a special section on counselor supervision. When combined with the highly recommended video from Kelly Productions, *A Chink in the Armor* contains everything needed to run this unique program.

Ordering and Information

We invite you to utilize our special BookCrafters Ordering and Distribution Center *for ordering only*. For general questions and information about Kelsey & Co. Publishing, please see Information below.

Book Orders

US and Canada:

Please call our BookCrafters Ordering and Distribution Center toll-free at 1-800-879-4214.

International orders:

For international orders please call (313) 474-6991.

Representatives are available to take your order from 8:00 a.m. to 11:00 p.m. EST, Monday through Friday (except holidays).

Information

For general information and to find out more about our exciting upcoming titles, write to us at Kelsey & Co. Publishing, P. O. Box 1138, Santa Cruz, CA 95061-1138 or call/fax us at (408) 457-9011, or email us at: kelsey1co@aol.com

About this book Byron Lewis has blended the best of neuro-linguistic programming and cognitive behavioral-therapy into easily understood and pragmatic tools for working with addictive disorders. This book provides the counselor with specific techniques to initiate and support early recovery from alcoholism, drug addiction, and other addictive disorders. As in his first book, Byron takes very complex concepts and makes them simple and easy to use. Peppered with entertaining and informative illustrations by Leslie Lewis, this volume is a must for anyone working in the field of addictive disorders.

About the Author Byron A. Lewis, M.A., earned his undergraduate degree in psychology in 1978 while studying at the University of California at Santa Cruz under the tutelage of John Grinder, one of the originators of NLP. He received his Masters degree in Marriage, Family and Child Counseling with special emphasis on NLP and Transactional Analysis in 1980. An international trainer in NLP, Byron's work in the field of addictions began in 1985 while employed as a civilian for the US Army's European Alcohol and Drug treatment programs. In 1993, he became the Director of Monterey County Health Department's Day One outpatient perinatal and adult treatment programs. He currently works as an Analyst for the Monterey County Health Department and as a consultant to the California Women's Commission on Alcohol and Drug Dependencies.

Notes

Notes

Notes

Notes

Notes

Notes